WeightWatchers®

SHOT in the ARM

SHARON LEE RIGUZZI

A daily dose of motivation for your weight-loss journey

ABOUT WEIGHT WATCHERS

Weight Watchers International, Inc. is the world's leading provider of weight management services, operating globally through a network of Company-owned and franchise operations. Weight Watchers holds over 48,000 weekly meetings where members receive group support and education about healthy eating patterns, behavior modification and physical activity. Weight-loss and weight-management results vary by individual, but we recommend that you attend Weight Watchers meetings to benefit from the supportive environment you'll find there and follow the comprehensive Weight Watchers program which includes food plans, an activity plan, and a thinking skills plan. In addition, Weight Watchers offers a wide range of products, publications and programs for those interested in weight loss and weight control.

DESIGN **ANN-MARIE WALSH**

ILLUSTRATION **CINDY LUU**

FOREWORD

*I*often speak about the perils of being a people pleaser. Ever since I was a little girl I've felt a need to win people over and go all out doing good deeds. I was popular of course! But keeping all of the focus on others also enabled me to avoid dealing with myself.

Sometimes all my people-pleasing was not enough to make me happy. Then I'd turn to food.

It wasn't until I became Weight Watchers spokesperson that I finally understood that my weight problem was actually rooted in my emotions. What a revelation!

And right from the start Sharon Riguzzi took me by the hand and helped show me the way to a better life. There isn't a day that goes by when I don't use one of Sharon's many pearls of wisdom. Sometimes I just want to ring her up for a good laugh. And even then, I listen to every syllable.

I am so delighted that Weight Watchers has compiled a collection of Sharon's wisest bits and published them as "Shot in the Arm." Her words are truly inspirational and sure to brighten your days. I absolutely adore Sharon—and I know you will absolutely love her book.

Love,

[signature]

THE DUCHESS OF YORK

In memory of my best friend,
Janet Sullivan, and in honor
of all the strong women who are
part of the fiber of my life.

INTRODUCTION

I began writing these motivationals as the year 2000 was arriving. I wanted to give my members something to look forward to, and I called these mini-essays "A Shot in the Arm." They were about trying to encourage friends who were attempting to lose weight, and I hoped a weekly Shot would help them. But a funny thing happened after I had written about a hundred. It hit me that I was really writing the Shots for me—to keep me focused. If once in a while someone else got something from one of them, all the better.

Over the years I included a friend or friend of a friend to my Shot e-mail list. And she would tell a friend and...You get the idea. Over the years the list has grown to hundreds of people from all parts of the country and all walks of life. While the Shots were designed to motivate others to reach their Weight Goals, people found they helped them in many other areas of their lives. I hope they give you that Shot of inspiration.

SHARON RIGUZZI

TABLE OF CONTENTS

A Very Good Place to Start

It's springtime, and I find myself in Germany surrounded by mountains literally right out of *The Sound of Music*.

If you've never seen the famous movie, you and my husband would get along great. I, on the other hand, grew up with it—it was the first Broadway play I saw, at the age of ten. When the movie came to the local theater, I most likely was the first kid in line from my neighborhood.

So to find myself driving through those

mountains, being a stone's throw from Austria, seeing real edelweiss, is a surreal experience. The only thing that would make it better would be having the sound track playing while driving. Of course I could sing the whole score, but I am trying to be considerate of the driver's ears.

Rodgers and Hammerstein sure knew how to put into words and music so many of our thoughts.

> *Let's start at the very beginning,*
> *a very good place to start.*

Nowadays we don't want to start at the very beginning. When it comes to reaching our goals, we want to skip the intro stage, hit the fast-forward button, and get to the finish line ASAP. But so often we miss some important information by not wanting to be a beginner—a beginner will get more guidance because others will want to help him or her succeed.

> *Besides which, you see,*
> *I have confidence in me!*

While this song isn't one of the more popular

Rodgers and Hammerstein tunes, I love it, and over the years I have often found myself humming it. You've heard of Positive Self-Talk? Well, this is positive self-hum, and I swear it has helped me through many hurdles.

> *When the dog bites,*
> *When the bee stings,*
> *When I'm feeling sad,*
> *I simply remember my favorite things,*
> *And then I don't feel so bad!*

What wonderful advice! We need to introduce all of those people we know who seem to attract the dog bites and bees stings in daily life—and then whine about them—to this song so they can learn how to cancel out the bad thoughts simply by thinking of their favorite things. What are yours?

> *Climb every mountain,*
> *Ford every stream,*
> *Follow every rainbow,*
> *Till you find your dream.*
> *A dream that will need*

All the love you can give,
Every day of your life,
For as long as you live.
Climb every mountain,
Ford every stream,
Follow every rainbow,
Till you find your dream.

Sorry. I did start singing.

We often use mountains as metaphors for the challenges in our lives. As I stare up at these mountains that were a real challenge that many people, not just the von Trapp family, had to climb, I am awestruck. Here it is a beautiful, sunny day, and their jagged peaks are covered with snow. And there isn't just one of them. How did the von Trapps do it? Did they ever feel discouraged? I'm sure they did, but they kept going. They probably gave each other support. When one started lagging behind, another must have offered a hand to help pull them along.

What are your mountains?

When you find yourself getting discouraged, what steps do you take to keep moving in the direction of your Winning Outcome? Do you turn to others for support? If you don't, shame on you. I often hear people (including myself) say, "I had to do it all by myself!" or "Can you believe not one person offered to help?" or "I couldn't do it. I had no help at all, and it was more than one person could do alone!"

Do we think it's a sign of weakness to ask for help?

Here's a tip: Most people are more than willing to help; we just have to ask! So today, right now, ask for help. It will make it easier for you to get closer to your Winning Outcome, and you'll probably have some time to do some of your favorite things to boot!

Numbers Game

I never would have considered myself a numbers person. If someone starts a conversation about the stock market or finance, I zone out. Numbers, I would say, don't interest me. Though as a child, when someone asked me how old I was, I would say, "Nine and a half." Or it would sound really cool when a few months slipped by and I could proudly say, "Nine and three quarters." Or how about the day after you turned twelve, when you could say, "I've started my thirteenth year"? I stopped this nasty habit many moons ago—well at least, twenty and a half years ago.

If asked, I would have denied I was a numbers person. But then again, when asked, "How much did you lose so far?" you would hear me say, "Thirteen and a half pounds, but I still have thirty-six and a half more to go." This clearly was before we learned about Positive Self-Talk.

Let's stay with the numbers theme for a minute. My knee-jerk reaction is to say I have no interest in the stock market, because I really don't like to gamble. The thought of losing something I worked so hard for would make me say without hesitation, "No, thank you!" if someone asked me to invest in a sure thing.

And yet, I have been a gambler. For years, I would gamble every weekend. Not in Atlantic City, but at restaurants, at the family dinner table, even in the car. I would gamble away a week of hard work, saving for my dream (Weight Goal). And then I would go to my meeting, weigh in, and say in an incredulous tone, "Only a half?"

I also gambled as if I were at the track. I might win by a mere hair (a smidgen of a weight loss). I wasn't happy, but I wasn't upset enough to change my odds. That is, until a Leader once said to me as I got off the scale three quarters of a pound lighter,

"If you lost this weight without really trying, can you imagine what you could accomplish if you really put your mind to it?"

What a wake-up call. Someone once asked me how could she get the discipline necessary to do this. I think it's a little like the chicken-and-the-egg dilemma: Do you need to want it so much that you are able to focus on your Winning Outcome and the discipline will follow—or vice versa? When you're saving for a new car, do you call it discipline when you put money aside for the convertible? When you're saving for a trip to the Caribbean, do you call it discipline as you put money aside for the beachfront villa? Are you halfhearted about saving for these things? No! Because they are things that you want!

Remember: Can you imagine what you could accomplish if you really put your mind to it? Anyone interested in taking on that challenge?

Just Do It Now

Do you ever make deals with yourself? Like when the clock radio is nudging you to wake up, you think, "I'll hit the snooze button just one time, and then I'll jump right up and get started on the day." Or when household chores are begging for your attention: "I'll just telephone so-and-so first. Then I'll roll up my sleeves and tackle this stuff."

Well, at least you and I don't use filler tactics like watching reruns of shows we've seen a thousand times! Or eating a Twinkie just to finish the box! I hear some people do that!

Seriously, why is it that when certain things—and not necessarily difficult things—pop into our minds, we become like cars that stall. I know it isn't in hopes of someone else picking up our slack and rescuing us from our to-do items—that only happens in fairy tales. We know that eventually we are the ones who will have to do the dirty work. Yet we dig our heels in till the very last possible minute.

Let's examine this phenomenon:

- It has to get done.
- It is our responsibility.
- We put it off continually, all the while fretting over the fact that it has to get done.
- As the deadline approaches, we rush to get it done.
- Once done, we feel really good about it.

When you think about it, it's pretty silly to be keeping ourselves from feeling good. Is there any logic here?

There are so many articles written about making lists and prioritizing. And most make perfect sense. (I've even read a few of them when I was putting off doing a chore!) Yes, the list-making and checking-off process works for many people—and there's even the proven advice of doing the difficult items first. Sounds good to a lot of folks—but doesn't exactly make me want to jump out of bed.

For years I handled my procrastination problem by doing one chore and then rewarding myself. (I still use this technique once in a while.) In any event, the first step to solving a problem is always admitting there is a problem. I'm ready to admit! Don't let me be alone, dear readers! It isn't important that we all have the same plan of action. What's important is to have a plan that we stick to.

The folks at Nike have the right idea: "Just Do It."

Let's make a pact to tackle our "put-offs." One a day for a week would be an accomplishment that would make us all experience number 5 on that list. Are you up to it? Are you ready?

Say! I just did my one for today! And I feel great!

Dream Catcher

I spent a few days this week up in Massachusetts and was able to explore the coastline. As I was walking along the deserted sandy beach, it seemed that I was a million miles away from New York and all that has happened in the past weeks.

It seemed peaceful. It seemed soothing.

But then I felt myself pulling away from being encompassed by these much-needed comforts. Why should I benefit from feeling good when so many are still suffering? As I scanned the horizon, my eyes came upon a lighthouse. Watching the beacon flash slowly, steadily, I was hit by the realization that I needed to be exactly where I was at that given moment. For the last few weeks I was just on automatic pilot. Doing what needed to be done, but not looking ahead. Bobbing along, treading some water. Staying afloat. But not looking to see where I was going.

How many of us feel these same feelings when it comes to achieving our Winning Outcomes? Our goals may seem trivial in light of all that happens around us. We might feel like we're slipping a little further away in some cases, then in another moment inching closer again, only to be caught in the current of ambivalence. I have heard some people felt themselves experiencing a form of unconscious self-sabotage, doing little—and sometimes big—things that would push their dreams further away.

It's as if we feel we don't deserve our dreams. We all deserve our dreams.

Each and every person who lost their lives on September 11 had their own goals and dreams. But they were cut short. But I am sure none of them would have wanted any other Americans to be kept from working toward their dreams.

We don't have to go stand on a beach to look out for a lighthouse to give us direction. It's as if in each one of us is a lighthouse, a beacon that will help guide us. We just have to trust our inner resources and listen to them. We may get lost every now and then, or misguided and confused, but we can look to our inner resources to get refocused. And if we sometimes feel we are all fogged, give a yell. You are not alone, and there is always someone floating nearby to give you a hand.

Giving Gifts

The time has come to sell the car, but before we put the ad in the paper or place the "For Sale" sign in the rear window, we take care of those pesky annoyances we've been ignoring till now: the broken taillight is replaced; the front passenger door that hasn't closed properly since the car left the showroom is realigned; the ding in the back passenger door—the souvenir from an on-the-loose shopping cart—is popped out and touched up.

While we're at it, what about the house? This might be a good time to put it on the market to see how much we can get for it. But first let's throw a coat of paint on the outside; fix the shutter that's been hanging from one nail for ages; clean out the basement, the attic, and the junk drawers; get a plumber to fix the toilet that's been running and running and running; and...

Wow! Now the house looks so inviting—especially with that almost-new car in the driveway—that we find ourselves rethinking our initial plans.

The big question: Why does it take a major sell decision to get us to fix the things that have annoyed us for so long? The answer: When we believe the payout is worth it, we find the time.

Let's make ourselves worth it. It's the little things in life that bring happiness, but these are also the things that we let go. You say you're not handy? You've been waiting for someone else to do the fixing? A lot of times the repairs aren't complicated; they just need to be moved to the top of the list. Like losing weight. Moving them up improves the odds that they'll get done.

Little White Lies

I've been thinking about the awful habit of telling lies lately, and it has led me to think about a related topic: lying to yourself.

You might be thinking, "Well, I never lie to myself!" And good for you if that is the case. But before you go patting yourself on the back, please try on some of these proverbial shoes. Do any of these fit you?

- I really didn't want that job anyway!
- I really didn't want that stupid job anyway! (Adjectives can make us feel better!)
- I'll eat this and then get up every day an hour earlier to run 5 miles.

✪ "I like being this heavy. Who cares what others think?"

✪ "I'm just too tired to do _____."

✪ "I can never accomplish _____."

✪ "I don't think he meant to be so mean."

You may think these are inconsequential lies, but they leave their mark. One lie builds on another; soon we are believing the gibberish we're telling ourselves. It is as if we were applying a quick-working salve to take the sting out of the real issue: disappointing yourself. Some salve!

Lying to yourself is just another way of beating yourself up.

I am convinced that most times we tell ourselves these lies because we don't believe we deserve whatever it is we are aching for. From that first time we pined for the phone call that never came to the "thanks, but no thanks" letter we kept watching for, we should have been giving ourselves positive messages: "Okay. This didn't happen the way I had hoped. Something better is going to come my way."

Too many of us seem to have replaced Positive Self-Talk with the negative quick fix of "Who cares anyway?" Eventually we will become believers that things don't go our way because we aren't worth it.

But it's never too late. The next time you realize you're lying to yourself or making derogatory comments about yourself, shout, "Enough is enough!"

Are you still uncertain? Still struggling with questions like what makes the other person get the job instead of you? Or the other person lose weight before you do? Or someone else achieve his or her dream before you realize yours? Most times it is due in large measure to their belief in themselves. We are all pretty good at getting upset with a friend or loved one who settles for an outcome. We can see their unhappiness. So, why is it so difficult for us to recognize when we are guilty of settling for less than our goal?

Let's put down the white flag of surrender. Let's stand firm and arm ourselves with an arsenal of beliefs and truths that will mow down any negativity that comes our way. Is this a hard path? Possibly. But it can't be any worse than sitting on the sidelines, looking at others who have accomplished what we want to achieve.

I'm here to tell you: Dreams can come true. It just starts with accepting the simple truth: You are capable.

And you wouldn't call me a liar, would you?

Incoming Curveballs

Instead of my usual Thursday-morning ritual of writing my Shots, I found myself rushing to the airport to catch an early-morning flight. Driving into the rain-soaked darkness filled me with trepidation as I fought back the thought that my flight might leave without this passenger.

Arriving at the airport, I reached to grab my suitcase, laptop, and pocketbook. Did I say pocketbook? It doesn't matter if you call it a pocketbook, purse, or handbag—there wasn't one sitting on the passenger seat next to me. This brought my mad race to a sudden halt. I realized that my arriving on time meant nothing without a little item called a picture ID, which was still sitting at home on my dining-room table.

My first reaction was to use some Negative Self-Talk—"You stupid idiot!" came to mind. But I quickly snapped out of it since I knew it wouldn't help the situation one iota. What I needed was a game plan: Do I turn around and go back, do I call and ask my loving husband to make the same treacherous journey to the airport, or do I just sit down and have a good cry? My choices were many.

Taking a few deep breaths, I decided to take my dilemma to an expert. For once, not being a perfectionist paid off. As I rummaged through pockets, I found a credit card and some papers that allowed me on the plane as long as I didn't mind security really searching my suitcase. A bit calmer, flying to my destination, I had another "oh, no!" moment. How do I rent a car without my license? Again my dear husband came to my rescue, by faxing my license to the car-rental counter.

My first thought was to keep this morning of obstacles to myself, but I decided to share it because people like to know others also make mistakes and have difficulties, and maybe we all can learn something from my angst.

Thirty thousand feet above the snags I had encountered, there was brilliant sunshine and blue skies. What a difference from the rainy mess I left behind.

So often when life throws us a curveball, we want to pull the covers over our head and escape. Or we feel life isn't fair, and why do these things have to happen to me? We spend more time wallowing in our misery than trying to find a way out.

In the past this would often be my MO, but eventually I realized this behavior didn't move me to a better place. We often think the discomfort we are feeling is more tolerable than the fear of the unknown, whether it's having to work really hard or asking others for help and possibly being turned down. Things can always get better; we just have to take an active part in making the first move.

So if life throws a detour in your way, here are a few steps to help you jump over the barricade:

- Breathe.
- Stay calm.
- Try to find the humor in the situation.
- Tell yourself things could always be worse.
- Ask for help if you're stumped.
- Take action; don't wallow.

These roadblocks are the ones that you probably will laugh about someday, but I say, "Why not laugh about them right now?" A laugh or two will definitely help you release some of the stress, and although people around you might think it a bit odd, you'll feel a whole lot better.

Great Intentions

During this past month my husband and I had two firsts that made us feel old. Our two eldest kids and their spouses had us over to their new homes (as in houses with mortgages, leaves to rake, rooms to paint, electric bills to pay—which has made them actually turn off lights when they leave a room!). On the drive home from two equally delightful evenings, I remember thinking that I would send a little thank-you note to each of the couples, letting them know how proud their dad and I are of their accomplishments.

That was about three weeks ago. Did someone say the best intentions...?

Last Sunday I thought that this week I would be able to start fitting more exercise into my life by getting up at 5:15 instead of 5:45 each morning to walk.

Does your alarm clock have a snooze alarm?

I wrote in a few of my Christmas cards to old friends, "Let's make sure we get together this year!"

That was the same message I wrote to these folks in 1995, 1996, 1997, 1998, and... What year is this? Do you think they think I mean it?

Now I know some of you are the organized souls who carry note cards with postage already adhered to the appropriate corner of the envelope.

This Shot is not for you. This is for the rest of us.

Sometimes a bubble of an idea comes out of my brain (like send a thank-you, get up earlier, get together with friends), and I actually see myself patting myself on the back as the idea pops up above my head. Unfortunately, it just as quickly evaporates into thin air.

Poof!

After a time lapse, I return to the same thought, but then instead of patting myself on the back, I see myself slinking away, filled with guilt because I know I didn't do that great idea. It never moved from a great idea to an action taken.

Here's the question: What is it that keeps us from doing something we want to do—even if it is after the fact?

Is it that we don't want to call attention to the fact that we didn't accomplish what we set out to do? Are we embarrassed? Is it that we no longer think it's a good idea?

I know some of you are squirming in your chairs as you read this, but isn't it a good feeling to know you are not alone? Here's my proposition:

The next time one of these bubbles appears over your head, go ahead, pat yourself on the back for such a good idea. But if it evaporates before you take action, the next time the thought pops up again, instead of slinking into a corner, do it now.

It doesn't matter how much time has passed.

So what if you didn't start that exercise the first week in January? Do it now.

You completely forgot about your decision to keep

a daily journal in that new book you got as a holiday gift? Do it now.

Remember the biggest lesson we all learned from 9/11, the day that changed our lives forever? Do it now.

Hey, I like this idea! I'm getting excited about it! But before I pat myself on the back, I have some thank-you cards to write.

Roses
Are Red

Valentine's Day has been a holiday that most of my life I have dreaded.

Through grammar school the fear that I had fewer valentines in the mailbox than anyone else plagued me from Feb 1 through the 14. Amazingly, in my teens if I did have a boyfriend, it seemed we'd start quarreling at the end of January, and by heart day I was usually sulking on the couch, watching *The Mary Tyler Moore Show* or *Rhoda*, thinking at least they would understand how I was feeling.

When I finally met the love of my life, I anxiously awaited our first romantic Valentine's Day together.

I can remember pulling the expected hearts-and-flowers card out of the envelope only to find instead a cartoon tiger saying something like

> *Roses are red,*
> *How 'bout a date?*
> *You make me laugh,*
> *I think you're great!*

(This was probably when my husband first started asking, "What did I do wrong?")

It finally dawned on me that there are very few people who could live up to the fantasy that I had conjured up in my romantic mind about what the best Valentine's Day should be. To keep from being disappointed year after year, Valentine's Day has a new meaning for me. Now it's the day I need to recharge my love of self. Now I can feel some of you cringing saying, "Yeah, right." But bear with me. We are all so hard on ourselves. If I asked you to list five things you don't love about yourself, you'd probably have a hard time narrowing the list.

Instead, I need you to do the following:

☺ Get a piece of paper. Fold the paper in half, and then, just like in kindergarten, cut a half heart away from the fold. (I can still remember the awe that filled me the first time my teacher told me to open the paper!)

☺ Find a red felt-tip pen or a crayon, or if none is available, a regular old pen will do.

☺ List five things you love about yourself. There are many more than five, but this is a beginning.

I'll wait.

Is your list finished yet?

☺ Draw a few hearts and arrows.

☺ Place this in a special place for you to view throughout the day...week...month...year.

Why did I ask you to do this? So much more can be accomplished when we are feeling good about ourselves. And yet so many minutes in the day we spend dissing (is that what the kids say?!) ourselves. Putting your heart on your bathroom mirror or in your date book or on your computer can be a constant reminder of just five of the many wonderful things about you.

We spend so much of our lives waiting for someone else to say wonderful things about us. And when they don't, we think there is something wrong with us. Folks, so often people don't say wonderful things about us because that isn't part of their makeup, or they don't know what we need to hear. (They missed the rehearsal scene in our minds.)

It's up to us to start telling ourselves the good stuff. Trust me, the more you do this, other things that you want to accomplish will start happening because you'll start waking up feeling you can take on more and start believing you are worth it!

Some of you haven't as yet gotten out the paper and red pen, and that's okay. I have faith that you will. You owe it to yourself to be your own valentine.

P.S. One of the items on my list that I love about myself is my sense of humor. I wrote this in big letters as a reminder so that tonight as I open up my Valentine's Day card from my honey and a monkey pops out, I'll react appropriately. After all, obviously, my sense of humor must be one of the things he loves about me, too!

Getting Lost

Recently I had the opportunity to drive a rental car that had one of those Never Lost contraptions. After watching its little training demo, I thought I would try it out. It seemed simple enough. Put on seat belt, start engine, punch in address of your destination. Within seconds I was no longer alone in the car, but was accompanied by a very pleasant female voice. She was very explicit with her directions, "Hard right turn in 2.8 miles." Every now and then I would somehow misinterpret her directions and go the wrong way. I did start to sense some annoyance in her tone as she spouted, "Recalculating directions," letting me know it was my fault we weren't exactly on track.

For the first few jaunts, as we would pass a mall or even a gas station, I would be afraid to stop because I didn't want to tick her off or, worse, risk getting totally lost.

When she would say with a sigh of relief, "You have arrived at your destination," I have to admit I was relieved. But by the third day I decided to risk—to dare to rebel. I was hungry, and although I hadn't typed in the address for Applebee's, I was going to intentionally turn off the prescribed path. Holding my breath and taking a non-directed hard right, I shot off the freeway. Gliding into the Applebee's parking lot, I turned off the motor before she could voice her dismay.

Enjoying a nice lunch, I got back into the car and started the engine, bracing myself for what was to come. Would I have to start all over again, punching in my destination? The Never Lost lady appeared. She came to life and very nicely asked me, "Would you like to resume your journey?"

Wow! No lectures, no cold shoulder, just a simple question, to which I punched in my "yes."

Wouldn't it be great if we could do this for the

journeys in our lives that take us to our goals? If each day when we got up, we dressed, did our normal routine, then stated aloud or wrote down what our goal for the day was and also our ultimate destination. Then we could jot down some of the steps that we know will get us going in the right direction.

If somewhere during the day we found ourselves veering off track or taking a total respite, when we finished, we could just ask ourselves, "Would you like to resume your journey?" No beatings with a wet noodle, no Negative Self-Talk, just a clean, swift "Let's resume."

Because let's face it: Only if you're driving with my husband do you start from point A, arrive at point B, no matter what might catch your eye along the way. Most of us get distracted, but we still make it to our destination. So what if it takes us a little bit longer? We might experience something that was enriching and worthy of our time.

Embracing Change

It's gone. For the twenty-five years I've lived in our town, it was there, and now it's no longer. If I think back, I might recall some whispers at a neighbor's cocktail party about its demise, but I ignored them in the same way I would have ignored a rumor that the man across the street was carrying on with the new mail woman. Preposterous.

Coming home from a business trip a few weeks ago, I approached our street in the same manner I had for more than two decades, and then I saw it — or, should I say, didn't see it.

Our blinking light was gone.

To some of you, this might sound like a who-cares

kind of occurrence. But to me this was a big deal.

The blinking light was probably first installed in the '60s or '70s in an attempt to get drivers to slow down as they went down one of the main thoroughfares in our village. The hope was it would help prevent accidents. But as everybody knows, over the years not much slowing down has occurred. So if I had been sitting on the recent committee that decided to dismantle the light, I might have even voted aye!

But that wasn't what the blinking light meant to my family.

Oh, no, it had a much more important role in our lives: When giving directions to a barbecue, holiday party, or sleepover, "turn at the blinking light" were the final words; when telling a friend you'd meet them halfway to go for a walk, it was always "Let's meet at the blinking light"; and when the kids were young, the blinking light was the limit for how far they could go without asking permission.

You are probably saying, "Get a life!"

What I did do was have a *Moonstruck* moment,

smacking myself on the cheek and yelling, "Snap out of it!"

I hate to admit this since I regard myself as a pretty easygoing, flexible person. Change is becoming a challenge for me. The lightbulb went off when I realized I'd been whining about my blinking light to almost everyone I'd encountered over the past three weeks. I'm always saying, "I love change," but now have to add, "if it's a change I want." Let's be honest, because I know I am not alone. How often do we hang on to a grudge; the ways things used to be; a disappointment?

Is it normal to voice some sort of dissatisfaction? Sure. But once is enough, and then get on with your life! So often people spend more time wallowing in the muck of the situation than they do trying to come to terms with it.

Here's a news flash!

People don't like being around moaners. It's not even healthy for you to be around the complainer if that person is you. You can get pulled further down into the hole of negativity, and climbing out becomes more difficult each and every day.

It is sometimes easier to continue to wallow than it is to embrace change, the unknown. And yet the unknown is chock-full of wonderful possibilities just waiting to happen.

My challenge to each and every one of you today is to answer these two questions:

What is it that you are having a hard time letting go of?

Are you willing to do what it takes to move on with your life?

Any time you hear moaning coming out of your mouth, have a *Moonstruck* moment (a light tap on the cheek will do, accompanied by a hearty "Snap out of it!"). The blinking light is gone. And the world goes on. Shouldn't we?

Get What You Want

This past Sunday my in-laws celebrated their sixty-seventh wedding anniversary. Yes, I did say sixty-seventh! Spending this amount of time with one person seems mind-boggling to most of us. When asked how they've managed to stay together, my mother-in-law replies, "We didn't know any better!" (Obviously keeping a sense of humor at all times has been a big part of their relationship!)

Besides love and hard work, I've witnessed a sense of commitment between these two. But it got me thinking: Why do so many of us shy away from this word in all different areas of our lives?

Some of the definitions I found for commitment might give us some insight:

commitment *n.* **1** the act of pledging or engaging; **2** the act of binding yourself to a course of action or another person; **3** the act of consigning a person to prison or a mental institution

I have a news flash for you: We all need a sense of commitment in our lives. Don't get nervous; I am not saying it has to be to another person. Let's start with gaining a sense of commitment to ourselves. We continually talk about goals, Winning Outcomes, and what we really want out of life. And the only way we'll ever get to the finish line is to continually revisit this subject.

So get your pencils ready.

What do you want, and what's it going to take to get what you want?

This is where it sometimes gets a little tough. We often don't like the answer to this question. It might take some hard work. But unless you are willing to make a commitment to yourself, I can almost guarantee you won't get what you say you want.

So how long will it take? I'm not asking for sixty-seven years, but I would like you to commit to one year (with an option to renew, of course).

What's it going to cost?

Time, focus, planning, Positive Self-Talk, Mental Rehearsing, and the most important— a good Motivating Strategy!

If you're not familiar with this last tool, picture yourself already having achieved whatever it is you set out to do—running in a marathon, building a house, losing weight, driving in your new convertible. Whatever your dream is, realize how good it feels to have achieved it, and then think back on the commitment it took. Once you've achieved it, the commitment is always worth it. It's important that we keep visiting the good feelings daily to keep us passionate about what it is we want.

You are definitely worth the commitment.

Don't be afraid of the commitment. We'll help one another along the way.

Dusty M&M's

Last week I went over to a co-worker's office to ask a favor when I happened to notice on her desk a glass candy dish containing eight M&M's covered with a piece of plastic wrap. This piqued my curiosity, so I asked, "Why do you have a piece of plastic wrap over the top of this dish?"

"So they don't get dusty," she replied.

My brain raced to figure out what she meant by "they." The M&M's? Never in my life have I worried about my M&M's getting dusty.

I spent the rest of the day marveling at this model of self-control, in complete awe that she could sit there and ignore the green one calling her name!

In fact, around 11:30 p.m. I realized that she probably had not thought about those M&M's since she answered my question, while I had done little else!

Let's analyze this for a moment.

My co-worker doesn't have a weight problem. She sees her challenge as keeping those M&M's dust-free until the next time she feels inclined to pop one or two into her mouth. My mind-set: It's ludicrous to save eight M&M's. After all, that's one handful in the mouth. Done. Gone. No more worrying about the dust situation.

Of course I have always been challenged by my weight (and M&M's). So I knew there had to be a lesson here to learn from my new idol.

The world is made up of all different types of people who go about their day in a manner to which they are accustomed. We all have idiosyncrasies, and I bet if we were asked about some of them, we wouldn't even know how they became habits.

But sometimes we get so caught up in doing things our way it's as though we have blinders on when it comes to being aware of how others handle similar situations. Well, guess what? We can actually learn from one another.

Try a little experiment this week: Raise your awareness, taking the time to observe others going about their daily tasks. If you notice someone using a clever idea to get a particular job done, don't be shy with the praise (everyone likes praise). Or if you see someone doing something you don't understand, ask questions. The point is people appreciate your showing an interest in them. At the same time you could be learning a new way of doing something.

So many of us struggle with our challenges because we keep attempting to overcome them in the same old ways. Instead of asking for guidance, we take a deep breath and think, "This time I'm going to do it!" But if we just repeat the same actions we've been taking, we're very likely going to repeat the same disappointing outcomes.

We could all use some shaking up in how we handle situations. Seek out people who have a different way of dealing with things. Be open to hearing their suggestions. You might find yourself embracing the same old problems in new, successful ways.

Now I'm off to buy some plastic wrap!

A Strong
Makeup

Disappointments happen every day, and yet some
of us don't even take the time to acknowledge them.
Weaving throughout our lives, always unwanted,
disappointments have worn us down but have
always left behind a strong fiber that was necessary
in our growth process.

I have always been amazed at people who take
on professions where they are guaranteed many
disappointments before they might possibly succeed:
actors, comedians, politicians, writers. A person
dealing with ongoing rejection or ridicule has
to have a strong makeup.

Most of our disappointments occur without the

whole world noticing, and yet even privately we try to fight back the tears or act as if we didn't want what passed us by anyway.

Life has taught me that even though we might be let down over a particular outcome, it normally is for the best. And yet when someone says that to us, we get annoyed at him or her, especially in our hour of wallowing. Do you ever stop to think, "If this hadn't happened, then I never would have been in this other place to take on _____?"

Many of us wouldn't have attended the colleges we did, do the work we do, be married to our spouses, if fate hadn't thrown an earlier disappointment at us.

As we age, we begin to acknowledge that we are not immune to disappointment; putting those times in perspective, we'll be able to move to a better frame of mind more quickly. Isn't having hindsight a great and mature skill?

We all deserve the best of everything. Unfortunately some of us get so discouraged we take refuge in our beds with the covers over our heads, giving up totally on a particular dream. This not only is an unhealthy way of dealing with things; it also enables someone else to grab our brass ring if we are no longer present in the game.

Let's take each disappointment that comes our way as feedback; learn from each experience and then revamp as necessary; not get discouraged, but keep in mind others who faced disappointments in life—Walt Disney, Thomas Edison, and so on (they didn't pull the blanket over their heads!);

Remain open to all possibilities.

This is what makes life exciting.

Becoming a Hat Person

I bought a hat the other day. An upcoming occasion
noted on my calendar just seemed to shout "chapeau."

Of course my brain kept reminding me that I was
not a hat person. Flashing back over the years,
memories were vivid of the snap of elastic under my
chin from many an obligatory Easter hat. And of
course having attended parochial school all my young
life positioned either a beanie or the ever-so-attractive
felt pillbox (it just didn't quite give me the panache
it did Jackie O) atop my noggin. So why did I find
myself in the hat department, plopping bonnets—
from the dowdy to the ridiculous—atop my head?
Because besides the giggles that I experienced (mine

and those of strangers who happened upon the scene), a sense of "maybe I can pull this off" bubbled up inside of me. My inner voice cheered me on: "What the heck? What's the worst thing that could happen?" Practice that Positive Self-Talk you like to preach: Take a risk!

Off I went to the affair, garbed from toe to head. And much to my dismay, my head was the only one that wasn't naked. As I scanned the room, searching for another brave soul, panic almost had me shoving my magnificent millinery into the nearest trash can. I wanted to be like everyone else.

Somehow I found the courage to continue walking, head held high. Bracing myself for some elbow nudging, whispers, and smirks, I looked for familiar faces so I could try to blend in. As the day progressed, I stopped counting the number of people who commented on my head wear: "You look so great in that hat!" "I wish I could wear a hat!" "You're so lucky to be a hat person!"

After the umpteenth time of replying "Oh, I'm not a hat person!" I finally stopped and just smiled.

That's when it struck me: How silly we are to convince ourselves that we are not a particular type person. Whatever the message we send ourselves— "I'm not a hat person," or "I'll never be thin," or "I'll never get that job," or "I'm not a dancer"—it can become a self-fulfilling prophecy. Granted, donning a hat is a bit less monumental than striving to make the cut on *American Idol*. Yet the same factor keeps us from expanding our horizons: We do not like to feel uncomfortable. Having stepped out now a few times as a more modern Hedda Hopper, I am beginning to enjoy being the person I thought I could never be. Dare to get out of your comfort zone and experience new things! You, too, can be a hat person and have everybody else thinking they wish they were as lucky as you.

So, try it! Take a risk! Sign up for tap-dancing lessons. Try Rollerblading. Get those funky glasses. Buy a hat!

Listen to Your Heart

I met up with an old friend the other day, someone I hadn't seen since college days. Granted, it took a rather lengthy conversation to catch up on jobs, kids, and so on. And then I asked her, "What else are you doing with your life?"

This question might have made some hesitate before speaking, but she didn't miss a beat as she shared, "Well, I've been doing some artwork. In fact, my work has been in a few shows."

Of course I was impressed and happy for her, but before I could share my congratulations, she continued, "Do you remember our grammar-school art teacher?" Amazingly, I did. An old toughie (of course, thinking back on it now, I realize she could've been my current age).

"Well," she continued, "one day in fourth grade as she was inspecting each child's artwork, she took one look at mine and declared that I shouldn't waste my time. I would never be an artist—absolutely no talent."

That message played in her mind throughout the rest of her school years, as she watched from afar as high-school students' work was showcased in the glass cases in hallways. That message followed her into adulthood.

Until one day just a few years ago, now a teacher herself. Sitting in the back of one of the watercolor classes her students were taking, she just picked up a brush and started playing. When the teacher walked by, he asked her how long she had been painting. Looking at her watch, she said, "Twenty minutes." Thinking she misunderstood his question, he asked, "No, I mean how long have you been painting?" Again she gave the same answer. "You're kidding me! You have such talent!" he said enthusiastically.

The floodgates of emotion opened, releasing what

she had always wished for but never dared to explore were being validated. And the rest is her history.

My purpose in sharing this encounter is twofold:

For all of us to recognize just how powerful our words can be, either to a positive or negative effect.

No matter what messages we might have received in life, if you hear a little inner voice trying to shout, "I've always wanted to _____," listen to it! Even if it doesn't work out, you are never worse off than you were when you were just wondering.

So many of us have gifts that we've never taken the time to explore, be it a comment someone once made or our own lack of self-confidence that keeps us from our dreams.

If I could share with you the radiance on the face of my friend as she talked about her passion coming to fruition, all of you would rush to create that for yourselves.

You deserve it, and so does the world.

Invest in Yourself

Flying back last night from my first trip to Las Vegas, the reality hit that I am not a good gambler. Too nervous and too chicken are just the beginning of the reasons why. Plus, jealousy ran through me every time I heard bells ringing and coins ka-chinging around me. (Granted those lucky winners probably put a lot more quarters into the slots than I did—but that's beside the point.)

Since I spent more time as an observer than as a risk taker, I came away with some learnings. These observations are based mainly on the slots, since the tables were out of my league (and comprehension!).

✪ For sure, these people have a Winning Outcome. They know what they want: cold, hard cash.

✪ They are very focused on the means to the end. They have chosen not only slot machines as the means but also a particular slot machine that they seem married to.

✪ They are patient, knowing they have to give the process time.

✪ They are persistent. They don't give up just because of exhaustion or if one day happens to turn into another.

Any of this sound familiar? I seemed to have that first priority down pat: I would like to go home with a wad of cash. My problems began with the second point. There was no rhyme or reason to how I selected a machine. After getting tired of looking at a bunch of oranges that didn't line up, I'd move to the next machine. I later—actually, not too much later—found out that was a big mistake. The realization hit the minute someone else sat down at what I now refer to as "my" orange machine and had the bells and whistles go off as an avalanche of coins swept them away. That was my machine! Those winnings had my name written all over them. Every time we passed the woman who'd "stolen" my machine in the hallway with her newly purchased jewelry, I would hiss at her under my breath. My husband would start squeezing my arm in the same manner that was used on one of our kids when we were trying to get their undivided attention. I soon realized he was right: I must've gotten caught up in the excitement of beginner's bad luck. I'm fine now. I'm over it. Really. (But that was my machine, and I should've won.)

This trip did show that I have the attention span of a three-year-old. I wanted instant results and after a few minutes (and dollars) on one slot, I would move to a new one on the other side of the casino. (Who says I'm not a fast learner?) Patience is not a word in my vocabulary. And persistence? We won't even go there.

It was then that I realized that the main reason for my not winning was based on one important fact: I really didn't believe I was going to win. The other gamblers knew they would win—it was just a matter of time.

I am not here to argue whether gambling is a good or bad thing. (Personally I would rather take the money and put it to a more solid investment— like dinner and a show.) I am pointing out that if we took these same four steps, plus the belief in ourselves, we could apply them to our other dreams and desires.

A lot of us go through life flitting from one slot machine to the next, never giving one enough time to hit the jackpot. First off, we need to be focused on what it is we want. And folks, this isn't the same as making a wish while we blow out the birthday candles—you won't make something happen just because you told someone what it is that you desire.

Say it out loud. Write it down. Concentrate on it.

Believe you can do it. Then blend in the patience and persistence necessary to keep at it until your bells and whistles go off.

Keep in mind that most of our dreams can't be given to us by someone else. We need to give these special gifts to ourselves. Life is too short and precious. Give yourself the gift you really want. Granted, whatever it is will take time—it's like a stock. You make your investment and then watch as it grows. (Hmmm, sounds a bit like gambling, too.)

Just invest in yourself. Invest in your dream. Then watch your best investment grow.

Seven Days ★

Don't you feel good when you go out of your way to do something nice for someone else? These things could be little things, nothing extraordinary, but big enough to improve the quality of someone else's life. You want some examples? How about these:

⊙ giving up your seat on a bus for someone older or a person loaded down with packages

⊙ telling a harassed sales clerk that you feel for her since she has so many people to service and she's doing a great job

⊙ sending a quick note of thanks to a colleague who helped you out when you were overwhelmed

For generations these old-fashioned acts were what we were taught to automatically do. Nowadays if you do any of the above, people might look surprised, if not shocked.

But think about the impact. That night at dinner while recounting her day to her family, there would definitely be a comment: "And then, out of the clear blue..."

None of us start out our day consciously saying, "Today I will have no time to do anything nice for anyone else." But in the midst of the craziness of life, it's not that difficult to do things for others, sometimes without their even being aware. What's the benefit? Besides what others might get from it, you feel good, and that in itself increases your ability to do the good things you have to do for yourself.

Seven niceties, one a day for a week—that's not too much to ask, is it? And there's a guarantee: If you fulfill this challenge, you will be able to tackle more of your own to-do's because you will start feeling a rush.

Are you up to the challenge?

Giving Back

Six months after 9/11, the line at the blood-donor facility still wrapped around the building and took hours to get through. People were told to come back at other times. In a time of feeling helpless, this was one way that everyone felt they could do their part. I always shied away from giving blood. I don't like needles; I'm a bit squeamish. But after watching my best friend go for chemo for years and being stuck up the wazoo, I felt I had nerve saying I don't like needles. Who does? It took Janet's death to move me to give blood a few times a year.

It's the least I can do.

Yet sometimes life fogs over that commitment

I've been meaning to keep. Some of you are already getting squeamish yourself because you're thinking, "I thought this Shot was supposed to make me feel good, not guilty." But the other day when I pulled into the blood bank's parking lot, there were empty spaces right up front.

The best intentions. We all have them. We try to do them. But often life doles out so many items into our packed schedules the things that we intended to do fall by the wayside.

Hey, it would be great if everyone reading this would run out and give blood, but that's not my purpose (although they do give out Lorna Doones—*3 POINTS* value for four!—and juice afterward). If each day this week you commit to doing one thing aside from your normal routine that would in some way make another person smile, you would be living up to the challenge.

Catch the Enthusiasm

This is an exciting week in our house. I have two children returning from college. One as a graduate (yea!) and one with two years down, two to go.

Next week is an even more exciting week—both of these dear ones start jobs (double yea!). I spent last night taking the grad shopping for the new professional wardrobe that she needs. Many dollars later we returned with an armload of goodies, and I have to say her enthusiasm was contagious. She's beginning a new avenue of life, stepping into the unknown, and she so wants to achieve all of the goals she has set out for herself.

I felt a bit jealous. How long has it been since I felt that sense of excitement? How long has it been since I have started out ahead of time to properly prepare for what I needed to accomplish?

Each week new members join Weight Watchers, and so many of them have that same spark of excitement. Granted, sometimes the spark doesn't appear the night they join, since there are so many other emotions floating around after that first experience at the scale.

But the next week, when they come back for their results, most times that starts the sparks flying! You also run into these same people in the supermarket, and their cart looks like it could be in a WW commercial! They're getting prepared. They want to be prepared for what they need to have on hand to accomplish their Winning Outcome.

My friends, almost all of us have been these members at one time or other, and then somewhere along the line we've lost the spark. We feel a bit jealous when newer members are seeing results, getting cheers, when we're on hold.

So if any of you can identify with this holding-pattern feeling, I have a proposition for you:

Clean slate. You're all new members.

We're all anxious to get started on something that's going to get us closer to our goal.

In fact, why not invite a friend to join with you? We all know that person who has been talking about their weight. It might make it a more enjoyable journey, and it's often a more rewarding experience as you catch the spark from a newbie. You might even become their guide and mentor.

The other thing I find interesting about my daughter Kate, the graduate, is the fact that she always believes she is going to achieve whatever she sets out to do (new clothes or not). How this child knew from the time she was a toddler what it's taken me my whole life to figure out (and revisit each and every day) is beyond me, but she has always known that she has all the inner resources she needs.

And whatever she wants, she just goes after it. None of this "I don't know if I can do it," or "What if everyone else is better than me?" or "What if I fail?"

These words, my friends, she has never uttered. She is not arrogant. She is self-confident.

So capture the Kate syndrome (she would die if she ever read this). The choice is yours, but I know which one I am making.

Real Heroes

Memorial Day is almost here: Barbecues will be held. Parades will be marched. White shoes will come out of hibernation. The sounds of kids playing outside after dinner waft through open windows. Weekly garage-sale flyers cover telephone poles so we know where to go to buy someone else's stuff that has cluttered their attic and basement for years. And for many, this weekend opens up the world of pools and beaches.

But with all of the excitement of the unofficial beginning of summer, I, like so many others, sometimes forget (or as is the case with so many of today's kids, don't know) what the Memorial in

Memorial Day signifies. This day started way back just after the Civil War as a time for us to honor and remember those who gave the ultimate sacrifice—their lives.

Most of you have heard of the play and movie *Six Degrees of Separation*. I'm bringing it up because I'm guessing we all know of someone, or know someone who knows someone, who has served our country. My suggestion for the week is to ask around at work, among friends, at your book-club discussions, "Who has lost a family member in service of our country?"

The purpose? To see that we all have been touched in some way—some closer than others—or other by these heroes. In their honor, tell the family member how much you appreciate our freedom because of brave people like their fallen soldier. At the same time we can be teaching our kids that we are so lucky.

So whether or not you have kids marching with their little league team, scouts or band, make it a point to go to the local parade to give your support.

And if you see an old-timer wearing a too-tight uniform or a faded army hat, stop and shake his hand, and thank him too. Watch him well up with pride. Because years ago he took action to get what we wanted; learned to recognize all of the wonderful traits each of us possesses; found the inner strength to make a difference.

And by your shaking just one veteran's hand, I guarantee you will make him feel great—and so will you.

Changing Times

I had a heart-to-heart with a very close friend of mine this week. This friend has been lamenting the fact that the long-feared time of life, menopause, has definitely thrown its net around her. The whole megillah—hot flashes, mood swings (although I admit I haven't really noticed them as far as she's concerned), insomnia, and the curse words to any one of us who is affiliated with Weight Watchers— weight gain. We talked for quite a while the other night. I listened to the string of "woe is me!" statements as they came out of her mouth: "Why does this have to happen? Isn't it bad enough that we're aging? Can't we do it sans the side effects? I'm doing everything I've always done on maintenance; how come it isn't working anymore? Maybe I should just get used to the new fluffier me."

In our past lives I would have suggested we go someplace for some sort of comfort food (ice cream immediately comes to mind). But with the arsenal of knowledge that we've both gotten from WW, I took her for our other favorite remedy—shopping.

Obviously I hadn't thought this through, since for the next two hours she was cursing her body, Mother Nature, the fitting-room mirrors, and the laws of gravity.

As we drove home, I realized I was about to lose it—my patience, that is. Try as I might, I couldn't keep from blurting out, "For gosh sakes, will you stop your bellyaching?" I quickly continued on, realizing that if she noticed I had said "belly" she would've been off on her "big stomach" tangent again. "What is it that has you so upset, and do you plan on doing anything about it besides complain? So what you've been doing isn't working anymore; get over it, and do something else!"

That shut her up, and for the rest of the ride home it was as if I had the car all to myself.

In fact, I did. (Please tell me some of you also talk to yourself occasionally.)

When I got home, I made a list of what it was that had me so crazed. I won't bore you with the list—it pretty much covered all of the above, with the following items added:

- ⚙ I work for Weight Watchers.
- ⚙ I have a lot of people who look up to me.
- ⚙ I've been able to maintain my weight for nineteen years—up till now.

As I felt some new Negative Self-Talk coming into the picture, I knew this was not what I wanted. I realized I needed a Winning Outcome.

I want to lose 8 pounds. Some of you might be thinking, big deal, what's 8 pounds? That's what I was saying back in April, when it was 4 pounds. If I continue on in the same manner, in a few more months it could be 12. (After maintaining for nineteen years, this is a scary possibility.)

Next, I needed to do a storyboard. It was

interesting to feel the overwhelming feeling lift away as I chunked it down:

- ⚙ Weigh in once a week instead of once a month.
- ⚙ Keep a journal (yikes, this one's hard for me!).
- ⚙ Go to a meeting as a Lifetime member.
- ⚙ Keep exercise going at least three times a week, preferably four.
- ⚙ Knock off the wine at dinner except for special occasions (and every night's dinner doesn't classify as a special occasion).
- ⚙ Stop putting salt on my bacon (in other words, lighten up on the salt).
- ⚙ Only Positive Self-Talk allowed!

Why am I sharing all of this with you? Well, those of you who have been coming to my meetings have probably already noticed that I believe in being honest (and have realized I'm just admitting to being human). I'm sharing this with you because part of me feels it's not a bad thing for all of us to realize life does throw us curveballs every now and then. And then it's up to us how we play the game. The choice is ours.

Now what happens if this whole thing blows up in my face and you get to watch me get fluffier and fluffier? Well, I guess it would be proof that I'm all talk and no action. You have all heard me say, "Weight Watchers works—as long as we work at it."

I've worked at it for a long time, and I am not going to let something as annoying as the change change me into something I don't want to be.

Obviously right now I have to put a little elbow grease (how many *POINTS* value is that?) into the equation.

Anyone care to join me?

Letter to a Friend

This week I did something I hadn't done in years: I actually took out some stationery and wrote an honest-to-goodness letter to a friend.

I bet if I took a poll, I'd find that it's been years since most of you (like me) even entertained such a low-tech idea as putting pen to paper! And that's why I want to share with you the amazingly good feelings that accompanied the whole experience.

First of all, once I made the decision to sit down and see if I still knew the how-to's of composing a letter, I was pleasantly surprised to see that letter writing was, as the saying goes, like riding a bicycle. It all came back to me: the salutation, the opening, the body, and the complimentary close. I say that with much gratitude to my grade-school teachers!

This was not the burdensome chore I had been anticipating. In fact, after the first couple of paragraphs, I found myself wanting to share more of what might be of interest to this particular friend.

After addressing the envelope and searching for a stamp (did the one with the flag send the right message?), I took it to the mailbox. And as I dropped the envelope through the slot, I actually felt proud of myself! How ridiculous! It was, after all, only a letter.

I was still patting myself on the back when a new and truly exquisite feeling began to take hold of me: sheer joy. See, I was picturing my friend's face as she received this letter. It would be a treat.

So many things nowadays are done in the fast-forward mode: there's E-Z Pass for our tolls, fast food for our stomachs, ATMs and online banking for our finances, and on and on. Or how about those one-hour photo services? The very thought of mailing film in a yellow and black envelope to a processing lab in Wisconsin would send some of us into apoplexy!

I for one could not survive without these speedy innovations. But I believe they also groom us to become more impatient—ever found yourself telling the microwave to hurry up? Still, we might be missing out on some positive experiences by taking the quick way to get to an end result.

Now I guarantee some of you are shaking your heads right now, and I know exactly what you're thinking: "Might be missing out on what experience? Waiting on a long line at the bank?" All right, maybe that isn't one of the experiences you'd be missing. But let's take a look at the fast-food scenario—it's probably one that we are all familiar with.

In the time it takes you to decide whether you want a super-meal 4 or 5, wait in line for delivery of the order, and then double-check your change, you could instead stop at the vegetable market and pick out some nice, healthful produce. And if there are other humans in the house, you could enlist some volunteers to help create a salad or stir-fry some veggies with protein.

You'd not only finish the night with a healthy meal but also get caught up on some conversation too.

Here's another example where positive opportunities may await you. Try phoning someone when you know they are going to be home instead of when you know they will be out. We all use this avoidance technique to some extent. But the interactive dialogue, which we might be dreading, could turn out to be a really good thing.

In writing to my friend, I rediscovered that the body of the letter was the most important and beneficial part—for me. And the same holds true for the examples I just gave. My point is that we spend a lot of time hurrying, a lot of time with our heads down as we review and check off things on our personal to-do lists, a lot of time possibly missing out on some really neat parts of life.

This week I challenge you to try blending some state-of-the-art processes with one or two from the past. This might slow you down a bit—and that might be a very good thing. Ah! The mailman's here. I have to go check to see if I've gotten any letters.

Unsolicited ★
Advice

"You know what you should do?" Doesn't your back
go up when someone offers unsolicited advice?

In fact, often the back goes up and the mind
shuts down when people start telling us what to do.
Is it a leftover response from the teenage years?
Or is it a reaction based on who is dispensing the
advice? We don't even realize that those of us
who hate getting advice sometimes are very free
with dishing it out. Of course we might be so
busy dishing out advice we aren't aware that the
receiver has shut us off.

There's a song title that describes this whole dilemma:
"Don't Should on Me and I Won't Should on You!" (Say this

three times fast, and you might get into a bit of trouble!)

The downside is that we have become a generation that misses out on some good recommendations because advice has gotten a bad rap. In the old days, people would seek out a sage's wise counsel. Nowadays it's hard to find a good sage when you need one. But this could be because we don't take the time to look in the right places.

There are people all around us with experience in whatever area we are muddling through who would be surprised and delighted to share their knowledge. Be it the elderly man next door whose tomatoes are better than anyone else's in the neighborhood or the maintenance man at work who can get the black marks off the tiles in ten seconds flat, people are flattered when you ask them to share their expertise.

Maybe that's the clue. We are only open to advice when we ask for it, yet most of us have stopped thinking with our noggin and asking for it when we need it.

Seeking out advice doesn't mean you have to take it. Just keep in mind how good you feel when someone asks for your counsel and then ignores your wisdom and does his own thing. It's so interesting that by taking another's suggestion, we sometimes wind up saving time, or avoiding mistakes, or seeing things from a different dimension, and at the same time that someone else is flattered that another person thought their idea was worthwhile.

How fabulous is that? Instead of isolating ourselves with our own frustrating dilemma, we might be one piece of advice away from success. And often the person who can enlighten us is the person we least expect.

Look around. There are sages all over the place who are just waiting for us to ask.

Go ahead. Take my advice.

It's Your Choice

In the summer the county fair in my town attracts throngs of people. Driving by, you can see the bright lights and Ferris wheel, and if you have a vivid imagination, you can almost smell the cotton candy.

As kids we all loved to go to the amusement parks or fairs, and yet each of us would arrive with different destinations in mind. Some would get on the line for the scariest roller-coaster while others would spend their allotted money on shooting the moving ducks in hopes of winning the huge stuffed animal as opposed to the consolation-prize Kewpie doll. Another group would head over to ride the camel or gather round the barkers, who would try to lure them into their tents to see the bearded lady.

For weeks before the outing, we would already be thinking and planning each step, from buying our tickets to getting on the bumper cars, to the ice-cream cone at the end of the day. Some would be contemplating the experiences while others would picture the U-Haul they would need to take home all they would win.

The choices were overwhelming to us. At the same time, that was exactly what filled us with enough excitement that we sometimes thought we would bust. The same is true about our everyday lives. There are choices all around us. But sometimes we get so caught up in the everyday happenings that we forget other possibilities exist.

Some of our choices might seem as scary as the roller-coaster. And that might just keep us from even getting on the line. Or if we do brave it, we might keep our eyes closed the entire ride and never see what it is that is making our heart race as the wind wraps us in. What a sad state of affairs it would be to take the risk to go on the ride but never be open to all the experience has to offer.

The gambler, however, would skip the rides, just for the thrill of nailing one of those lame ducks. Their joy came not from the experience, but from the end result. Maybe a mix would be best for an interesting life—a few joyrides, a little bit of playing your luck, and throw in some time at the fun house just for a few laughs.

Sounds good to me. Why not try a few new choices that might throw a little spice into your routine? The problem is we often think we have no other choice. The good news is we always do.

Fear Factor

It is interesting how the fear of the time it will take to do something so often overwhelms us and stops us in our tracks. And the fear doesn't always rear its ugly head when we first join but, rather, when we hit a bump in the road. That is, when the Negative Self-Talk—the "I'll never be able to do this" mantra—takes over.

Since I had been down this road before, the last time I joined Weight Watchers I tried to analyze the situation. This was my profile: Get discouraged, quit. I tried to find other things in my life that I had wanted where the results were far off in the distance and yet I stuck to it. Unfortunately, I came to realize that I wasn't big into working hard at things that were difficult to do. This realization didn't do much for my self-esteem either!

But I did come up with two things I did stick with: One is my marriage—which never seemed difficult to me but probably looked challenging to a lot of other people (especially to those who were older and wiser than me at the time!).

And then I had an aha moment: This never seemed difficult to me because it was something that I really wanted and felt was worthwhile to work at each and every day.

The second is the times when I was pregnant. Those of you who have never had this experience, bear with me and try to imagine. It was something I really wanted (similar to the time I joined WW). In the beginning I was psyched (similar to WW). I would get excited as my body started changing, and each week I would track my progress (similar to WW). I would need to buy new clothes because the old ones no longer were fitting (similar to WW). And then somewhere during this wonderful experience I'd hit the wall, and I'd want it over! The time would start dragging, and so would I! People would look at me as if to say, "You still haven't had that kid?" (just like WW—"You still haven't gotten to your goal?").

Now the big difference between being pregnant and being on WW is, of course, I couldn't say, "I'm not doing this anymore!" I had to hang in there, but ultimately I reminded myself that having children was something I wanted.

So the last time I joined Weight Watchers, I decided to think of it like it was a pregnancy. I told myself I would give it nine months—it took ten—because I knew from experience that if I wanted to, I could hold out for that long. This commitment, along with coming every week no matter what was what, finally made the plan work for me.

Anyone for pickles and ice cream?

Make Believe

Having recently returned from a conference in Orlando, I would be remiss if I didn't talk about the amazing man who put this city on the map. In the past I've touched on Walt Disney's perseverance, not giving up on his goal although he received over three hundred loan rejections. Now that takes stamina! As I walked around the parks, surrounded by thousands of people, ages ranging from nine days old to probably one hundred, I was overwhelmed by Walt's vision.

I have always considered myself a visual learner, since I do much better seeing someone else demonstrate something before I can take on the task at hand. But vision is another story. How many of us can claim to have great vision?

vision *n.* **1** the ability to perceive something not actually visible, as through mental acuteness; **2** force or power of imagination.

As kids most of us were great at this. We would play make-believe, cowboys and Indians, war or house. When the double digits hit, well, let's just say I hope I wasn't the only one who sat looking through the Sears catalog, picking out all I was going to buy when I won the sweepstakes contest I had entered. And during your teen years I'll bet some of you were in the same boat as me, spending countless hours dreaming about the popular cute kid falling for moi. Through this formal analysis, can we all agree that the majority of us had vision at one time? So what happened to our vision, and what makes Walt Disney different from us?

He had his vision.
He didn't let rejection stop him.

He took action upon action.
He didn't listen to naysayers.
He didn't quit.
He really wanted it.
He believed in himself.

A lot of us have long forgotten about vision because we spend most waking hours trying to get all of the to-do's on our lists done (which doesn't ever seem to happen) and then we fall into bed exhausted to get some sleep before we start anew. We're often too tired to dream!

So get your pencils ready!

Brainstorm the top five things you would love to do (forget about the things you should do and have to do). Now brainstorming is an activity that usually takes more than one person, but since we all talk to ourselves, let's try this anyway, making sure that you place no judgment on anything you come up with. Remember, there are no wrong answers!

Once you come up with the top five, make a list of everything that accomplishing these five items would bring into your life—and I'm not just talking about material things.

Now make a list of every reason why you can never accomplish these top five things that you would love to do. Don't leave any out!

When this list is complete, read it over, and then take hold of it in both hands and proceed to rip it up into tiny pieces and dispose of it immediately!

Then pick one of your top five things, and do a storyboard on what steps you need to take to make the dream become a reality (it's so apropos to do a storyboard since this is the process that Disney used to make all of his cartoons come alive). Chunk it down to as many little steps as you can. (The smaller the step, the easier it will be to start checking off a step as it's completed!) Keep an index card with your top five listed on it on the visor of your car, on your medicine-cabinet mirror, in your palm.

Most of us probably don't have as grandiose a vision as Walt did, but our vision is important to us. So who are we to decide that it can't be done, or the body was meant to be heavy, or there is not enough time or money? Are you getting my drift? We are depriving ourselves—and possibly others—of the benefit of fulfilling something that we would love to accomplish.

So this week when you wish upon a star, make sure you follow it up with a lot of whistling while you work.

Don't Just Try

"Do the best you can."

I know I said this to a few people this week alone as they shared their concerns about upcoming weddings or vacations. Then I heard me saying it to me in the car this morning as I started to plan the rest of my week.

"Do the best you can."

I mulled this over and realized most of us don't really take this to heart. It often translates to "I'll try." Which often translates to permission to have more than you planned on having before you heard this phrase.

Let me give you an example. Think back to when

you were a teenager. If you wanted the car for Saturday night, you were told, "If you finish the English report that is due on Monday, then you can have the car." Not many of us were told, "Do the best you can and you can have the keys." It always goes back to the degree of our desire: When you want something really badly, your best is really what you do.

Here is my challenge to you: At the end of each day, ask yourself, "Did I do the best that I could today?"

If the answer is yes, bravo!

If the answer is "not really," don't beat yourself up. Instead, learn from it.

Ask yourself, "What can I do to make tomorrow closer to the best that I can do?" But remember this always has to be followed up with by a plan.

Think about it. You do your best for so many others— friends, family, work. Why do you shortchange yourself?

The Time Is Now

How many of you have ever taken the time to write down a list of goals?

I was surprised when I attempted to do this and it took much longer than I thought it would to come up with a Top Ten list of goals. Here's why: In the past when I made this list, I would do it just as an exercise, never believing these things would come to fruition. This list was of no greater importance than a grocery list, no great shakes if I didn't get to everything on the list. But this time I worked on the list more in the mode of thinking of my dreams and desires that I plan on accomplishing this year. Big difference, because I believe I can accomplish these things. And that's the key.

No matter what dreams and desires you plan on accomplishing, you need to believe you can achieve them, and you need to start this moment. Right now. After completing my Top Ten goals, I realized I've been craving more balance in my life, so I went back and labeled which goals were professional and which ones were personal. Interestingly enough, I have five and five. So this means I desire balance, now I just have to take action to make it happen.

No matter how much I wish my name were Samantha and I could just twitch my nose and accomplish my goals (some of us really did live in the best television era!), everyone of these dreams and desires won't happen unless I have a plan or what we like to refer to as storyboarding.

It's easy to get overwhelmed when we look at any item on our list (to lose weight, save for a car, pay off credit cards, spend more time with the family) because in this fast-paced world we live in, our biggest complaint is we don't have time!

I beg to differ with that lament. We never seem to have the time for our goals, but when someone else asks us for help, in many cases it's so they can meet their goals). While we may hesitate for a moment, we always find the time to pitch in.

Now you need to pitch in for your own Winning Outcomes. You need to take daily steps toward your dreams. It's exciting when you realize that these goals are within your grasp. They're yours for the taking.

Best Friend

This past Friday was my best friend's birthday. We were born exactly two weeks apart, and every year I relish the fact that she is a higher number than me for two whole weeks.

We made a pact years ago—no presents for birthdays or for Christmas. Our routine for getting around this rule, as we'd whip out pretty packages for each other, was to announce "This isn't really a gift. It's just something I saw that reminded me of you."

To me, having three daughters grow up in a house where Mom had a best friend was a gift in itself. Throughout the different stages of their youth, passing from one best friend to another, my children were able to observe our relationship and learn (much better than words could ever teach) what best friend means.

Best friend. How does the title get conferred? Do you wake up one day and decide to knight the other person Best Friend? It's more likely to happen when you're folding laundry late at night, waiting for the last load to be finished. The phone rings and you hear "How ya doing? You sounded like you had reached your limit when I spoke to you earlier, and I wanted to make sure you were okay."

Do you pick a best friend? Kinda. Sorta. We all tend to migrate toward people we like. My best friend and I? So much alike: similar backgrounds, similar values, similar features (in fact people have often mistaken us for sisters).

But I didn't know she would be my best friend when she was sitting in front of me in world history class, with her banana curls cascading down her back onto my desk.

My best friend and I? So very different: She's the smarty-pants with a Ph.D.; I passed. She's the nurse; I'm the married one. She's the athlete; I'm the mom. She's the daring one; I'm the spectator. She's the one my girls think is cool; I'm the "Mom, you're embarrassing me" kind of mom. She's the matching underwear and outerwear woman; I'm the elastic-stretch Lollipop and Hanes-briefs beauty. Back in the '80s, she was the purchaser of a new mink coat; I was into new storm windows. She's the stubborn one; I'm the "if it means more to you, I'll give in" kind of gal. She's forgetful of nothing; I'm forgetful of too many things. She's caustic; I'm wimpy.

Qualities to look for in a best friend? For me:

✿ Acceptance. Knowing that the differences are what make us friends even though they sometimes might drive us crazy. You may argue, you may fight (best friends know the difference between the two), but you always know that you'll make peace because what you have is so special and important to your life.

✿ Conversationalist. Talking to each other every day even though there is nothing new to talk about.

✿ Lucy-and-Ethel-isms. Like making macaroon cookies together when one of us can't tie the apron around a ten-days-overdue belly. (Do we even like macaroons?) Getting up in the middle of the night to be the first ones at an outlet sale. Making a gown for a ball on the day of the ball. Teaching my daughters the alley cat in my living room on New Year's Eve. Being able to have a sleepover and eat chocolate-chip cookies, drink cup after cup of tea, and watch TV all day with a big quilt covering the two of us at the age of thirty-one.

⊙ Sense of humor. Knowing your favorite time at special events (for example, weddings, dances, and reunions) is in the car on the drive home, when you talk about everything and everyone.

⊙ Loyalty. Knowing that no matter what you're doing, you'd drop it in a second if the other needed your ear, your strength, your support. My best friend timed my contractions when I went into labor. I took her to her chemo treatments.

This past Friday was my best friend's birthday. I didn't get her a gift because that's our rule. But I thought of her and began to write this. I know she'd approve.

In my mind and heart, my daughters are as much her girls as they are mine. She would want them to know that being a best friend is at times as tough as working at marriage or studying for a doctorate or having a baby. And that the rewards are immeasurable.

This past Friday was my best friend's birthday. She would have been fifty-four. She died eight years ago, but she is so alive in our hearts and in our home. I have many good friends. I may never have another best friend. And that's okay. Some people never have what I have had—and continue to have. Because she is here with me and with my girls. She left her mark, and she'd want it that way.

This past Friday was my best friend's birthday. I asked my girls to join me in honoring her by wearing matching underwear, eating chocolate-chip cookies, and drinking cup after cup of tea. She would be so proud of our girls, who are all adults. There's a part of her in each of their hearts. This is my gift to my best friend.

But it isn't really a gift. It's just something I saw that reminded me of her.

Take a moment right now to call, write, or hug your best friend. If they've already left us, spend some quiet moments honoring their specialness.

Rock the Boat, Baby!

Do you ever get the feeling that you are supposed to be doing more with your life than you are? Does the question from a popular song ever run through your mind: "Is That All There Is?" Even when you are content with your home life, job, family, and friends, sometimes that "what if?" question pops into your mind.

Of course the natural instinct is to squelch those rock-the-boat fantasies, not wanting to have a tidal wave or even a ripple affect the status quo. If things are running as smoothly as can be expected, why jeopardize the situation? And yet what if an idea or a dream keeps finagling its way into your stream of consciousness, challenging you to shift gears in midstream?

People who are unhappy with their routine often find it easier to switch gears and tackle new possibilities. As long as they possess a few important traits: a belief that they can accomplish it and the realization that they deserve a better life. It's more difficult for those people who aren't unhappy; yet turn down the volume on their inner voices. They're the ones who hit the mute button on the nagging messages and watch their life move in fast-forward. Before you know it, they're looking back at their lives and are wondering if they might've settled because it seemed easier at the time.

It's never too late to start enabling some hidden talents if your work ethic is as strong as your desire. Grandma Moses started painting in her eighties. For most people, there is always another choice; it's up to us to find the determination if we're up to tackling the steps involved. Think about it: The rewards could be a hundredfold. Do you want to miss the whole experience just because you were comfortable?

Time to Rightsize

Over the last few years the term downsizing has become an all-too-familiar part of our vocabulary. In companies around the country, while the employees are going along their normal routines, the news hits the streets that for the betterment of the company as a whole, this downsizing—or as a positive-thinking group called it, rightsizing—will take place. It brings with it changes, some good, some upsetting, but it should bring the company to a stronger and better place.

For a moment, think of yourself as a company. You have been going about your multitasking days for quite some time, sometimes feeling overwhelmed, frustrated, and possibly exhausted. And yet often as night falls, you look back on your day and don't feel that you've gotten any closer to the goals you have set for yourself. You fall into a troubled sleep where dreams take over, and you find yourself having a meeting with all of your top people (you know who they are), and the decision is unanimous that big changes have to happen to make this company—You—succeed.

As you lift your head off the pillow, you are ready to take action. It's time to downsize! I know some of you are thrilled with the thought of downsizing your bodies, your workload, your teenagers, but hold on a minute! Let's switch to the rightsizing mentality. Call a meeting with those old friends Me, Myself, and I and lay out the cards. It could go something like this:

"Listen, I'm going to be honest with all of you. I know you've all been overworked and frustrated, but we're still not meeting our monthly goals."

Allow time here for venting and some grumbling.

"Wait a second. I'm not saying I don't appreciate

all that you're doing, but I think we can all agree we sometimes feel like we're running around in circles."

At this point you should be nodding in agreement.

"So I think it's time for us to do a little rightsizing."

You'll hear a few gasps, but go on.

"Let's revamp how much time we spend on doing different activities, such as work, laundry, PTA, groceries, self-improvement..."

Okay, now it's time to let go.

Me can't keep quiet another minute: "Are you kidding me with those self-improvement goals? I tried to wake you up earlier twice last week, and you kept telling me to shut up and mind my own business."

"You are my business!"

"But I am not interested in taking any more abuse, so I threw in the towel."

You swallow and continue a little apologetically: "You are completely right, and I do apologize. I realize we are a team, and I had stopped listening to all of you when it came to feedback, but now I am willing to cooperate and not shut you out! And Me, it is getting lighter earlier, so if you try to wake me up to go exercise, I will listen because I know you're keeping the overall goal in sight. Will you give me another chance?"

Not sure if he should trust you entirely, Me finally agrees. The meeting continues with a total revamping of who is responsible for what. Myself volunteers to write down five personal things for you to accomplish each day. These you all agree will not be difficult things, but things that will keep you continuing on the same path (that is, having lunch someplace other than at your desk so you can take a breather, calling one friend each day who makes you smile, making sure you listen to something soothing during your commute instead of the news, and so on).

As the meeting is about to adjourn, Myself, who has been silent throughout, pipes up: "This all sounds fine and good, but the only way it's going to work is if you employ the iron rule." Seeing the confused look on the other faces, Myself says in a rush, "Well, you know how Mom taught us the golden rule—'Do unto others as you would have them do unto you'—and Dad introduced us to the silver rule—'Do for yourself as much as you would do for others'? I think our biggest problem is not listening to the iron rule: 'Don't do for others what they can do for themselves.' Not for nothing, this is why we never have time to do a thing for us—we're so busy trying to do for others!"

Sheepishly, they all agree and make a pact that they will start being more selective about what they take on. Me smiles impishly. "You know what? I think I'm going to like this rightsizing. It feels so right."

Take a Ride

I spent last week in Florida with very good friends and my youngest daughter, Kelly. We had a little mother-daughter bonding before she went back to college. Of course Disney was part of the week, and one day found us in the MGM Studios park, which I love. The Muppet show, no matter how many times I see it, still makes me marvel at the creative genius behind it.

But I have to admit I do have a small problem when it comes to some of the rides. My daughter wanted to go on Tower of Terror (or House of...I'm not sure; I just know the word terror is part of the title). One of my friends was nice enough to say she would go on it with her. Mind you, my baby is twenty years old and really doesn't need someone to go on a ride with her. She does meet the height requirement. But it is more fun to share the fun with someone else.

Being the good sport I am, I agreed to walk along the roped path until we got to where the elevator doors were in front of us. At this point they announce that if anyone has changed their mind and decided not to go on the ride, they can step to the right and they will be escorted to the lobby. I hadn't changed my mind since I had said from the get-go I wasn't going on the ride. This is not my idea of fun. I stepped to the right.

Once that ride was behind us, we meandered over to the Rock 'n' Roller Coaster, and my daughter started in: "Come on, Mom, it isn't that scary. Daddy will be so proud of you when he hears you actually went on this ride. Use a little Mental Rehearsal like you tell your members to. Mom, look at those little kids over there—they have to be six or seven— they're not afraid.

For some unknown reason, I decided to do it. I walked the whole line. I got right up to the ride. I started to back out, but my daughter started once again to psych me out, so I just got buckled in, closed my eyes, and started my Lamaze breathing (it's amazing how some things never leave you).

Now hear this:

I do not enjoy going on scary rides. I have made the decision that I will not go on scary rides anymore. I will not allow myself to be cajoled into getting on scary rides. I have no idea why anyone would think going from 0 to 60 mph in 1 second would be fun, and that was only the beginning. So, why did I go on it in the first place? I didn't want to be a wimp. I didn't want to be left out, sitting on the sidelines the whole day while everyone else has all the fun. I didn't want to disappoint my daughter.

Afterward, as I sat with my head between my legs, I thought, "Haven't I done the same exact thing with food in social gatherings? Don't I sometimes eat something just because everyone else is and I don't want to feel left out? Don't I sometimes eat a dessert someone made just so I won't disappoint them?"

Well, I've learned a few things at Weight

Watchers that have stuck with me: It's all about choices. I am a social eater, and I hate it when I am out with friends and someone might think, "Poor Sharon, she can't have any of these appetizers; she's on Weight Watchers."

It's all about choices. I can plan it in my day to have these snacks by eating lighter the rest of the day or by banking some *POINTS* values from other days or by earning some Activity *POINTS*. Whew! Some may say that might involve some work, but I say it's worth it if I don't want to feel deprived in a social situation.

It's all about choices. It took me a while, but I finally got past the "I made this dessert just for you" lament. If I want it, then I have it. If I don't want it, I either take it and don't eat it or use a handy excuse like "I'm going for a cholesterol checkup tomorrow—that would surely set me off the charts!" Or other favorites: "Thanks, but I couldn't eat one more thing!" or "Would you mind if I take it home with me for tomorrow night?" (and then try to conveniently forget it).

I used to always worry about hurting people's feelings until I realized after many visits to the scale after having given in to a hostess's begging that they would've gotten over it if I had just chosen to say "no, thanks." But here I'd be looking at a higher number on the scale midweek and I would start to get angry at the hostess and at myself for being the wimp.

I know in my heart of hearts it usually isn't one dessert that puts the weight on but, rather, the snowball effect that starts with eating the one dessert, the thinking "Well, if I've blown it, I might as well have..."

It's all about choices. It's time to listen to your inner voice as opposed to the others around you. Start having conversations with yourself before you eat something. "Is this something that fits into my plan? Is this something I really want? Is this something I won't regret later?" In the past I would start the conversations after the food was eaten: "Why did you eat that? You didn't even want it. It wasn't even that good. You're pathetic." (Such wonderful Positive Self-Talk!)

It's all about choices. So you may be wondering,

"If you know all of this, why did you go on the ride with your daughter if you really didn't want to?" Well, sometimes I am a wimp. And who said I'm perfect? And sometimes I need reminders—we sometimes get caught up in doing what everybody else wants to do, and we forget to go after what we want to do. From here on, I'll remember I actually want to sit on that nice bench under the tree while everyone else hops on the ride.

It's all about choices. What do you want?

Team Spirit

As I am not a golfer, it was with more than just a little trepidation that I awaited the Fourth Annual West Point Charity Golf Outing. Organized by my husband, the event raises funds to assist soldiers' families. Four of the helping hands belong to my kindhearted friend Cathy and yours truly. We were reassured by the organizer that, as recruits with most-favored status, we didn't have to really understand the game. We just had to look and sound as though we did.

We were in charge of special events at the second hole. Cathy, up on the green, quickly mastered her role. With tape measure in hand, she won the

complete respect of all the players. As for me,
I hawked various activities and collected money.
What do you think of my spiel: "Make sure you're
in for the fifty-fifty!" "Will you win closest to the
pin?" "Five bucks a chance, right here! You can
have a mulligan for another five bucks!"

Now, honestly, don't I sound like I know what I'm
talking about?

In between pitches I managed to take in some
aspects of the game and learned that best-ball
was the game being played. (Huh? I thought it was
golf.) When I asked about best-ball, someone in
the know explained: "Each player on a four-member
team takes a turn hitting the ball. The team decides
which of the four players had the best shot, and
then all of the members move their balls to the
location of the 'best ball' and hit again. And then
the entire process gets repeated. See? So simple,
a child can pick it right up!"

Hmmm. Well, I got the general idea. Basically
everyone wanted their team to win, but camaraderie,
not competition, was the order of the day. Everyone

was having fun. People were cheering for one another and especially encouraging the beginners as they moved their not-so-perfect shots to a place right on the green (a place they probably had only seen before in their dreams). Eventually I deduced that one of the best things about best-ball is how it lets team members make the less-experienced golfers feel more at ease. Best-ball is a wonderful illustration of teamwork.

Looking back at the event, I am sure there were one or two golfers who weren't real crazy about that best-ball arrangement; they would have preferred to claim their glory as individuals. But I wonder how many of us consider ourselves good team players in life?

My definition of a team player includes not being out for yourself and being able to share ideas and pitch in and work toward a common goal. A team player also is one who notices when someone else on the team is flagging and gives some extra assistance without being asked. It may well be possible that some people are natural team players. And of course there are some claiming the label who would be quite surprised to learn how others view their role as team player.

The good news is with a little effort we all can earn the team-player title and help our teams to thrive. Getting started is easy:

⚙ Recognize that so much more can be accomplished when we involve the whole group.

⚙ Be aware of the variety of strengths in the team, and use them to full advantage.

⚙ Share ideas and opinions, but once the team has a plan, embrace it.

⚙ Encourage teammates.

⚙ Pull a fair share of the load and, at times, even more than what's fair.

These precepts can be applied to our professional lives—and work just as well with the group around our kitchen table or the circle of friends with whom we spend our free time. Everyone benefits from teamwork.

By the way, I'm looking for a foursome for next year's outing. Anyone interested in being on my team? Only good team players need apply.

Giving Thanks

Thanksgiving. It's like a giant stop sign right in the middle of our zany holiday comings and goings. Thanksgiving. Stop and reflect.

Businesses are closed, and stores are darkened. Folks are either in their kitchens stuffing the turkey or wedging the homemade pies into strategic spots of the car to ensure safe delivery to the aunt whose turn it is to play hostess.

And we each have a favorite part of the day: the parade, the meal, the football games, the nap, the sandwich afterward. But topping any and all of these things is our personal list of things to be thankful for. Everyone's list is different. Some may be longer than others. And some people might have a hard time starting a list. A dear friend of mine has had many health setbacks over the past few years. One might think, "The poor thing. What does she have to be thankful for?" But I assure you this woman's list would go around the block because she sees the goodness in the things most of us tend to overlook.

To not take things for granted is easier said than done for so many of us. Why is that?

Let's take a heads-up from the happenings around us and use this holiday as a means for sprinkling our thanks not only into the mound of mashed potatoes before us but also into our conversations with the brother we never got around to thanking for picking us up in the rainstorm the night our car died, the kid sister who always babysits on a minute's notice, or the elderly uncle who served in World War II.

This Thanksgiving let's broaden the focus of our thanks beyond the masterly concoctions gracing the cornucopia tablecloth. Let's include the people who are surrounding the table and even those loved ones who couldn't make it.

We are a bounty unto ourselves.

Celebrating one another is much less fattening than second helpings of pumpkin pie but can sweeten the occasion beyond belief. It's worth trying, and mark my words, everyone will give thanks.

Mixed Messages

"I'm losing you!"
"You're breaking up!"

A few years ago who would have thought these phrases would become a part of our everyday conversation? And yet if you use a cell phone, you probably hear or say these words every now and then. A few years ago my friend Ann had taken a trip to Israel, and one of the peculiar sites she saw was everyone on a cell phone. I remember laughing and thinking, "Why would anyone need one?"

And now I have to admit that if I left my house in the morning without money, my lunch, my pocketbook, I would be able to manage. But if

I discovered I'd left my cell phone on the kitchen counter, I would have to turn around to retrieve it. You see, my friends, my cell phone has become a habit.

I'm not quite sure how this habit became so quickly part of my life, but it has. And just like most habits, I sometimes overdo it.

"I'm losing you!"

Isn't this also a phrase we say to ourselves when we don't want to listen to our inner voice? You know, the voice that knows what we really want, not just what we want at the moment.

"You're breaking up!"

This is how we ignore our once so-determined Winning Outcomes, and the more we tell ourselves these two phrases, we begin to forget that we had once had our hearts set on them. I call this false messaging. It's the same thing our kids do to us when they come home after their curfew, saying they never heard us say "in by 11." ("You're breaking up.")

It's what we do or say when we don't want to do what we originally had set out to do. Other false messages: "No time!" "It doesn't really matter."

Hmmm, in this fast-paced world, it is very easy to see there isn't time to do all of the things we want to do. But isn't it amazing how, when we want something really badly, we're able to fit everything in no matter what?

Just One Thing

Do one thing every day that makes you happy.
So reads a sign that hangs by the light switch in
our bedroom. It's been there for over a year, and yet
until recently I realized I hadn't seen or read it
lately. (I'll have to check with my husband to see if
he's ever noticed it!) This pretty plaque, like so
many other things in our lives, has become part of
our environment rather than the important reminder
that I thought, one day in a crafts store, we needed.

So many of us are programmed to finish this
(mowing the lawn, doing homework, cleaning our
room, doing one more load of wash) before we
can do that (go to the beach, go golfing, go to bed).

If there's enough time when we finish, we get to reward ourselves by doing what we love to do. So often we know even before we start the project that there probably won't be enough time to get to the fun stuff. How can this fact not influence how we take on the project at hand?

This doesn't just pertain to chores around the house. Take it one step further, to the workplace. How often do you think about working on an area of your job that really taps into that passion that first brought you to your field? But each and every day, once you step into your work boots, the thoughts vanish until you are on your way home, thinking, "Well there goes another day that I didn't think once about the niceties I wanted to start working on."

And should I even bring up our self-improvement list? Every time I hear someone (and that someone is sometimes in my head) lamenting how if only she had more time in the day, she would be able to get in the exercise; stop smoking; eat healthier; plan better; go back to school; take dance, flying, tennis lessons.

Most times these laments come from people who do eighty-seven things in a day, take care of fifty-four other people each day, and are so responsible that everyone depends on them.

Do one thing every day that makes you happy. So what's keeping us from accomplishing what we want to do? We can say lack of time, the immensity of it all, fear, lack of focus or belief in ourselves, Negative Self-Talk...Need I go on? It could be one or all of the above. And yet we have the power to change all of those barriers if we want something badly enough. In the meantime, we can chunk it down and start by using this mantra:

Do one thing every day that makes you happy. And maybe after doing this on a regular basis, you'll find you are doing five or six things every day that make you happy. You see, I am a firm believer that you create your own outcome. You have the power to make your day a happy experience. Since some of you might not be ready for that, let's stick with the basics:

Do one thing every day that makes you happy. Try it, I guarantee you'll like it.

No Whining

There must be an invisible sign floating over my head that reads "No Whining." People who know me are well aware that I have little tolerance for complaining. Of course my children all went through different stages of whimpering but eventually learned that these displays were falling on deaf ears. Colleagues at work were quick to grasp the fact that I am impatient with "woe is me" personalities.

Before you label me unsympathetic to people's plights, consider that I am always willing to assist someone with a dilemma—that is, as long as that person is willing to work toward the same Winning Outcome. Complainers wear me down. They seem to be able to zap my energy with even just one long-winded gripe session.

My response to venting? Don't complain to me. If you want to bring me a problem, along with it bring some suggestions for making things better. Otherwise we just waste our time in a vicious cycle of the unfairness of life.

Uh-oh. I just realized something. I've been complaining. I hate complainers.

If I were to tape my conversations for a day or two, you would notice that I am guilty of the same offense that, when demonstrated by others, I would condemn. Why are we so quick to list our physical shortcomings but not to pick up on the signs when our own personalities or psychological imperfections come to light?

I'm not a big complainer, mind you. But in retrospect, even my little offenses must be annoying to those listening. I complain when it's cold (I know in my soul I was meant to live in a warm climate). I complain when the alarm clock goes off before it should (how do the hours during the night fly by so quickly?). I complain when my French fries aren't piping hot (if I am going to eat one of my favorite foods, they have to be at their very best). I complain when my adult children don't call home to let me know they're alive. I complain about the sad fact that I had to be the sibling who always had to be challenged by weight. I complain when my husband buys cheap toilet tissue. (Is it because women use it more often that we know how important squeezably soft can be?)

These are just a few of the complaints that I can think of off the top of my head (how scary). Since there can be learning in every situation, here are some thoughts:

When we are shaking our heads at others' behaviors, we need to take a moment to reflect on our own imperfections.

Recognize these situations as opportunities to raise our awareness toward improving our attitude and idiosyncrasies so as not to annoy those around us.

Make a commitment to bite our tongues the minute we feel complaining words rushing to escape from our mouths.

Replace them with more positive statements, and eventually (after much practice) this will become the norm. (A lot of whining is just fill chatter—silence is better).

I'm up to the challenge. Are you? Let's see how many people we can shock with our positive attitude. (Thank heavens I've already purchased the correct toilet tissue supply!)

Banana Boat
Adventures

Spending last week in the Caribbean with all of our kids and their spouses left us with wonderful Kodak moments. Watching everyone getting along and enjoying one another's company warmed my heart.

Since I am not fond of the water, it took days of my kids' begging me to be adventurous, to be daring, to live, before I finally broke down and dived in (well, maybe it was more baby-stepped in). Seven of us saddled the banana boat—my pregnant daughter was able to be the photographer. As our "no problem, Mon" speedboat driver crisscrossed and turned, they were chortling; I was screaming. While they were switching seats with one another,

I was keeping my eyes shut, clutching on tight as we bounced over the waves. Eventually everyone fell off except me—Esther Williams (if you don't know who that is, you're probably too young to read this). That is, technically I didn't fall off. It was more a case of hanging on by one leg and a death grip (forget Esther Williams, think Lucy Ricardo).

As the family returned to the boat, they faced the task of pushing me back on the banana. One was pushing, one was pulling, I was still screaming. One tried to instruct, and another tried another tactic. All the people onshore probably thought this was some sort of boat show. Finally I was back on top of the banana for the revved-up ride back to shore.

Once back on solid sand, one of my kids asked, "Why were you so scared?" I replied, "I felt like I was drowning. I hated not being in control."

Another daughter blurted, "Mom, didn't you realize you were wearing a life jacket, which would keep you floating? And besides, don't you know we were there to help you, and we never would have let anything happen to you?"

When did the roles reverse? I missed that memo.

Do you ever feel like you're drowning? Do you ever feel you're losing control? So often in life, with the pressures of work, family, responsibilities, I sometimes feel like I am going under. And yet my daughters' questions made me realize what had been my main problem in the salty sea. Yes, I was afraid, but my carrying on had blocked my senses from recognizing that help was close at hand. All I had to do was reach out and calmly ask for it. My screaming prevented me from hearing offers of how we could accomplish our feat (and getting me on the banana boat was exactly that.)

I'll make a pact with each and every one of you. The next time any of us feels like we are drowning, we will take the following steps:

- ⊙ Breathe.

- ⊙ Look around to see who is available to help.

(If no one is in sight, make a few calls. This might take a while, especially if our MO has been "I can do it myself!")

⊙ Ask for help.

⊙ Let them help.

⊙ Forget about not wanting to bother anybody else. If they asked you for help wouldn't you pitch in?

I rest my case.

After the fright of the banana-boat experience left me, I realized I was proud that I actually had done something out of my comfort zone. It energized me so much that I suggested we all go on the water trampoline.

Who knew it would take more out of me than the banana (and I'm just talking about climbing the ladder). But that's another Shot.

Been There, Done That

It's a phrase we throw around a lot in our everyday conversations. All of us have different "Been There, Done That" lists. Mine consists of things like camping where there are no showers, watching scary movies, heating the house via a wood-burning stove. My husband's list would probably read something like going to the ballet, attending a Jack-and-Jill shower, eating a frozen dinner (on second thought, he probably has never had the pleasure, but if he should, I'm confident it will make his BTDT list).

Now think about your list. I bet you noticed right away that there is a common thread running in all our lists: Experiences we have labeled even more emphatically than never again!

Been there, done that. Just four words, but what a clear, no-nonsense message they deliver. It's our own short-talk for "sorry, buddy, ain't no way I'm gonna go down that road again!" So here's what puzzles me: Why is it that some of our most negative experiences never make it to this list? Examples, anyone?

How about a time you might have overeaten, had too much to drink, driven too fast, spent too much money, got too much sun.

I know I've experienced some of these events more than once. I even recall being a young adult, lying in my spinning bed at 3 a.m., moaning "never again!" Now I would love to tell you that once the bed stopped spinning, I "never again" had too much to drink—but I can't. Suffice it to say at that time immaturity kept the extra cocktails coming.

As for an overeating experience, let's just say I do have some memory of thinking "never again!" as I undid my pants button on the car ride home from a social event. But I never thought about putting these items on my "been there, done that" list. After all, I love food, and I do enjoy a social cocktail or two. So how could I possibly add these things to a list that has such finality?

The lightbulb just went on above my head.

If I want to put a stop to a negative behavior, it might help to pare it down. Take the overeating, for example. Although it isn't possible to take food out of my life totally (thank goodness), it might help to discover where in my daily experience eating turns into overeating. Is it when I go back for seconds? Or is it the unconscious eating that gets me into trouble? Unconscious eating makes me feel out of control, but what I really react to is that feeling of being overstuffed. That's the "been there, done that" experience I want to eliminate from my life.

I know just putting unconscious eating on my list

won't stop me from overindulging, but it's a start. It will raise my awareness. It will remind me that I hate the feeling of being stuffed and of not even remembering what it was I ate that caused this feeling. Putting it on my list will remind me that I hate this bloated feeling as much as I hate spinning beds.

So the next time a friend asks if I want to go to the new all-you-can-eat buffet in town, I'll be able to answer, "Been There, Done That. And never again!"

A Coat of Bravery

Halloween. As a kid, I wasn't crazy about this holiday. Sure, I loved the end result—loads of candy—but, oh, the process I had to go through to get there! Back then we didn't have store-bought costumes, and although my mother had many talents, whipping up ghosts and goblins on a sewing machine was not one of them. And I never understood why we said "trick or treat." What trick could I ever have performed if the home owner hadn't wanted to give me a treat?

Trick-or-treating after school was okay, but once I became old enough to go out with the big kids, I felt those butterflies hatching. The big kids ranged from twelve to seventeen. Their booty bags held some candy but mainly stored eggs for mischief making. That was a change for me, and not one I was at all comfortable with. The dark, damp, cold nights thrilled many of my pals, but I was a little intimidated by the whole thing. I just wanted to run to the houses I knew, feel my bag getting heavy, and then head home—with an occasional stop at an unfamiliar but friendly-looking house where I might land just one more Hershey-with-almonds bar.

My point: Even though there was an element of fear, pushing for just one more treat kept me in the doorbell-ringing loop a bit longer. It may seem sensible trying to avoid unpleasant or intimidating processes. But I wonder about the good outcomes we may be denying ourselves. How many of us let the dislike or fear of a process stop us in our tracks, preventing us from enjoying the end result?

If a major deterrent keeping us from accomplishing our goals is fear of the unknown, we can gain valuable insights from the Halloween-costume theme. When children dress up as Spiderman or

Superman, they start flexing their muscles, jumping from tops of bunk beds—in general, acting in a way they would not have dared to before donning the tights. But the truth is they always possessed the ability to do more adventurous things. They just never knew it. The costumes give them a coat of bravery.

Each of us possesses the ability to accomplish the Winning Outcomes we dream of. Maybe if we take on the persona of an individual who we think could easily reach that goal, we'd have more of a chance of getting through the process. I often use Helen Keller as my role model. She must have had fears about accomplishing things, but she didn't let them rule her destiny.

We all have the ability to achieve what we want. It's our own self-belief systems that either keep us in the house handing out the treats or place us out in the running for the reward. Don't let your mind trick you into standing on the sidelines applauding others as they achieve their dreams. There are enough treats for every one of us.

What are you waiting for?

The Power of Three

Is it an Irish thing, or is it just a superstition passed down from generation to generation that bad events always happen in threes?

When my grandmother would get word of someone's dying, she would say, "These usually come in threes." This would always be said with an air of authority, so I would just hold my breath and hope I wouldn't be part of the equation. As I matured, I found I would use this same phrase when speaking of appliances breaking down or lightbulbs burning out (nothing really life threatening), and since there was never a time line attached to the statement, it was easy to eventually shake my head as the vacuum ceased sucking dirt and say, "See?"

Back in December, I got word that my beautician had broken her wrist. Of course I sent my sympathy her way but selfishly was a bit concerned with how long she would be out of commission and the impact this would have on me or, more specifically, on my hair.

Then several months later my mom fell and broke her wrist. Of course I showed her the empathy she deserved and even accompanied her to her physical therapy a few times. When she voiced her frustration about the recuperation time, I would sweetly tell her, "Have patience!"

It didn't occur to me that this might be the second part of a trio until I found myself sitting in a Massachusetts emergency room with a swelling wrist.

The echo of my "Have patience!" keeps replaying in my mind. How easy it is to give that advice to others, as opposed to taking it personally to heart.

It took me a full sixty seconds to realize all of the things for which one depends on having the use of both hands. Little things that we take for granted, like buttoning a shirt, shifting the car into drive, tying one's sneakers, writing a weekly Shot in the Arm, and so on. Everyday events that we all do without thinking twice would make a very long list.

Of course amid all of the empathy people have been showering upon me, there come sprinkled phrases such as "This might be a sign that you should slow down."

Do we learn from such events?

Although I don't believe slowing down is always an option, we can certainly have other learnings. Appreciation is the big one that keeps crossing my mind. It isn't practical to think a year from now I will still take joy in cutting up my own meat. But I can assure you that when this cast comes off, I will brag to a waiter the first time I do perform such an activity.

As I watch a friend pull a sweatshirt over his head without even a second thought, I am filled with longing. Let's not take for granted those everyday occurrences that fill your day. Since I completed the trilogy of the broken wrists, you can breathe a sigh of relief!

Moderation, Moderation

I recently found myself thumbing through
(as opposed to clicking on) Mr. Webster's book
in search of the meaning of moderation.

My tendency is to read through the list of
definitions and then pick out the one I like best.
This is the same approach I take when going
through the fortune cookies on the table after
a nice Chinese dinner.

In this case, I read:

moderation *n.* **1** a moderating, or bringing
within bounds; **2** avoidance of extremes; **3** absence
of violence; calmness.

My eyes immediately locked onto that last word. Calmness. Now that's something I need to incorporate into my life.

Let's each take a moment to reflect on our lives. Do we even know what calmness is? The definition that caught my fancy when my finger finally rested on the word was

calm *n.* tranquillity, serenity.

How nice that sounds!

It has taken many years for me to realize there is a difference between tranquillity and boredom. And during these same many years a habit I have developed is to always fill in a blank space on a calendar with another project. In fact, this habit is what made me realize that if I want moderation in my life, I have to work toward making it a habit.

Some of us approach life in the same way we approach an all-you-can-eat buffet, piling as much as we can onto our plates. Sometimes we can manage the load; sometimes we make a mess of it, spilling things or making ourselves sick. We've learned that it's healthier to eat more veggies and less carbs, fats, and proteins, and yet when we get into some situations, we push that knowledge to the background. "I can handle it!" we tell ourselves. Four hours later, we are popping the antacids.

That same personality attends a meeting at work with an already full plate and by the time the meeting is over, leaves trying to balance an overflowing pile of projects. "I can handle it!"

Now I am not suggesting that everyone stop pitching in where help is needed. (After all, my co-workers read these weekly Shots!) My recommendation is more along the lines of agreeing to work on a project (be it heading up a task force at work, or getting five loads of laundry done at home, and so on) but asking for either the help of others or more reasonable deadlines.

Moderation. It sounds like a word my mother would have used (and one that would have put a frown on my adolescent face). Nowadays just the thought of the word makes me yearn for a smidgen of it. (I always suspected Mom knew best!)

Moderation equals calmness. These are the days I would pay money for an hour of just that. Calmness equals tranquillity. (Be still, my heart!)

We often hear "Be careful what you wish for." Even I am smart enough to know that too much calmness or tranquillity in my life could turn me into one very bored human being. That is why the church sign now makes so much sense. Everything in moderation, including moderation.

This week let's strive for a little bit of moderation in our home life, in our work life, in our eating styles, in our shopping expeditions, in our activities.

Think about the benefits. This might be better than a Calgon bath.

It's worth a shot.

Elbow Grease

Have you ever felt frustrated? (Please say yes!) It seems funny to say that my frustration is aimed totally at the computers in my life! At work we are having some technical difficulties, which make it very stressful to meet deadlines.

So I head for home, make myself a cup of tea, sit down at my very own beautiful laptop (I'm hoping flattery will help!), and it, too, betrays me and starts doing all sorts of kerflooey (not sure if there is such a word but think it's better than what I really want to say!) things.

That's it! I've had it! The frustration builds. I hate feeling frustrated.

For me frustration often equals quitting. Throwing in the towel. Lying to myself and saying, "Oh, well, I didn't really want to do that, or get that, or be that person's friend anyway." When really what frustration brings with it is some extra work, or as my grandmother used to say, the need for some elbow grease. Most things in life that are worth achieving come with some amount of frustration. Once we achieve them, the abundance of elation and self-satisfaction that accompanies the outcome more than compensates for the stress we had been experiencing.

I think it's good to vent when we're frustrated. And we all have different ways in which we go about the venting process. Some yell. Some exercise. Some cry. Some call a friend. Some write a Shot. And then it's important to find another tactic to reach our goals.

Venting ad infinitum has no purpose other than annoying all of those around us. So when you feel frustration enveloping you, take a moment to search for a tingle starting in the bottom of your spine.

This frustration can be a turning point for you. You can either throw in the towel, deciding you didn't really want it in the first place, or you can take a deep breath, vent a little if you must, and then readjust your game plan because you know deep in your heart when you complete this task, you are going to feel so good.

Whew! That feels better.

Harvest Reflections

On the one hand, it is hard to believe that autumn is here; on the other, as we wake up to dark skies and feel a briskness in the air, we know it is a fact.

Just as the squirrels are gathering their food for the next season, we will be collecting the last remnants of our vegetable gardens for canning or freezing, to keep a taste of summer in our meals throughout the upcoming months.

Mr. Webster provides a couple of definitions for the word harvest:

harvest *n.* **1** the time of the year when grain, fruit, vegetables, etc., are reaped and gathered in; **2** the outcome of any effort.

Does this mean that even those of us who have never set foot in a garden can be referred to as harvesters? Absolutely. If we scrutinize the outcomes of any of our latest endeavors, we will uncover our personal harvests. I believe to be viewed as a true harvester, we need also to see if the results are as good as we envisioned, and review the environmental variables (for example, did weather, timing, or lack of attention to detail have an impact on the final result?).

A true harvester wants to learn from the year's shortfalls and starts planning now for the next planting. In fact, some will even begin experimenting today with possible variations to ensure better bounty.

A lot of us harvesters have been working toward similar goals: getting healthier, becoming more active, getting more organized, slowing down, improving in a hobby (be it tennis, golf, sewing, crocheting, cooking, rolling pennies), sticking to a project until it's completed.

When asked about our progress in any of these areas, we might shrug and say, "Well, the weather hasn't been cooperating," or "I haven't had enough time to concentrate on it." I think it all comes down to two key questions: What's the bounty worth to you? What are you willing to do to make it real? A true harvester will work night and day. We sometimes voice our wants but don't follow through with the determination to do whatever it takes. Our best intentions can be plowed under pretty deep when we ignore them or give in to the traps that lie in our path. How badly do we want to reap the rewards of our efforts?

The richness of our personal harvests is up to us. With some perseverance, the rewards could be great. Let's not watch from the sidelines as others reap the benefits of harvesting exactly what they planned because they stayed focused on the end result and were willing to make it happen. Let's step out from the sidelines and take our place of honor.

Let's go for it!

Thanks, Mom

As has happened so many times in my life, a call
from my mother turned things around for me
a few years ago. Mom casually mentioned during
one of our daily phone conversations that she had
come across her list of goals for the year 1999.
She proceeded to read from this list of about ten, and
as she did, I was saying "bravo!" after each item.
We talked about how terrific it was that she could
give each one a big checkmark and exclaim "ta-dah!"
(This is just our way of doing a high-five on the phone.)

So let me list my learnings that my wonderful
mother has taught me:

Her list was written down; mine was in my head.

I used to write mine down but got too discouraged when I'd look back and see that I once again had failed to do what I set out to do. So evasive lists have become the rule. I may not remember everything that I wanted to accomplish, but, hey, how upset can I get when I'm dealing with the intangible?

Her list was a mix of some toughies and some "hey, I can accomplish that if I put my mind to it" goals. Her list did not contain one "if I have enough time, then I'll..."

The number of items on her list was not overwhelming.

She was able to locate her list so she could do some reflection.

Her list was from 1999! What, you may ask, makes this a good thing?

So many of us are guilty of giving up when we see we haven't accomplished what we set out to do. Fact: Some of the items on Mom's list she hadn't been able to check off right away. Instead of giving up, she continued. If she hadn't, she wouldn't have been able to give a final "ta-dah!"

Now who would like to join me?

I am making my list.

I am writing it down.

I am putting on it a mix of goals so that it won't seem overwhelming.

I am limiting the list to approximately ten (some people like to-do lists of one hundred—I'm starting small, but feel free to do what works for you).

I will put this list in a safe place. Uh-oh, those words scare my kids, since I am always looking for things that I put in a safe place. Let me rephrase that. I will put a copy of my list of goals for the year in a variety of places (in my date book, by my office desk, on my car visor, and so on) so I can refer to it before next year.

I will continually use Mental Rehearsing and Motivating Strategy to help egg me on.

I will use Empowering Beliefs on a daily basis. (If you don't believe you can do it, you won't succeed.)

If I were really brave, I would share my list with you now.

Once again, "Thanks, Mom! It is amazing to me

how you never stop teaching me things by example. One of my perennial goals is that I have as much of an impact on my children as you have had on yours." (Obviously that isn't one that you can check off and say you're done!)

Do You Believe?

Believing—it plays a key role in our lives. Over the years we believe in so many things, some of which have to make us smile! Santa, for example. I really don't have vivid memories of sitting on his lap, but I absolutely remember writing him letters, being sure to use my best penmanship. Even if Santa didn't bring everything I asked for, I chalked it up to his having so many children to take care of. I believed.

Should I even bring up the Publishers Clearing House sweepstakes? Please, someone besides me, fess up to imagining the doorbell ringing and trying to look surprised for the camera crew! And when we don't win, we still conjure up a wonderful winning scene for the next year's drawing! Why? We believe.

How many of us were brought up to believe that people are basically good? Even in today's topsy-turvy world, we still find ourselves looking for the good in all humans. Once again, we believe.

So here's the question: Why is it so hard for us to believe in ourselves?

Let's take a look at the last twelve months: Did we ever belittle or give up on ourselves? The fact is just about everyone has self-doubts. But let's not take comfort in that. Instead, let's learn from it. You and I believe in other people. We probably spend quite a bit of time building other people's confidence so that they can believe in themselves. Obviously we know how to walk the talk for others. Now it's time to start believing in ourselves!

Yes, this is easier said than done. Believing in oneself does not happen overnight. It takes days, weeks, months, to make it a reality. Let's start gearing up for the task at hand!

Here's a bit of pre-work:

○ What is the most important thing that you want

to accomplish this year? (Let's start with one item and move on from there once we get rolling.)

⊙ Picture yourself having already achieved it. Take notice of how great you feel and how happy you look.

⊙ Storyboard the steps that it will take to make this a happening.

⊙ Start each day reminding yourself "I am achieving my winning outcome! Today I will take the steps necessary to get closer to it." (If you're forgetful, write this on an index card and tape it to the medicine cabinet. And taping another one onto the car visor couldn't hurt!)

⊙ At the end of each day, praise yourself. (If others are around, you might want to do this in private. People tend to feel intimidated when another person is in earshot.)

Repeat these steps for the next 365 days, and you'll experience marvelous results! The fact is, you already have all of the resources necessary to make your dreams come true—and you don't have to sit on an old man's lap to make it happen. What better gift can you give yourself?

The Joy Magnet

About ten years ago I was attending a conference upstate, and as I stopped for a cup of caffeine on my way into the facility, a woman on line in front of me started a conversation. This little lady had to be close to eighty and here she was dressed in bright colors, makeup on, hair styled (and this was at 7 a.m.!).

We were doing what so many of us do in this situation: "Looks like it's going to be a beautiful day!" As I grabbed my cup and turned to say "Have a nice day!' this lady touched my arm, looked at me with sparkling blue eyes, and said, "Honey, read my shirt! I always have a good day!" She pushed her shoulders back like a soldier so I could read the calligraphy across her chest: "Don't Postpone Joy."

Another time I went outside at lunch to take a walk around our office building because it was an unusually warm and sunny day for March. As I was passing a woman walking in the opposite direction I said, "Isn't this fabulous weather!" She kept walking but started shaking her head: "We're going to pay for this!"

Both of these women had an impact on my life.

The first woman I think of often. How much of our lives do we spend thinking about

"when I lose weight, I'm going to..."
"when I get some free time, I'm going to..."
"when the kids are grown, I'm going to..."

The second woman reminds me of how much time we spend worrying about what's going to happen as opposed to being in the moment and enjoying life.

This is my challenge to each and every one of you: Look around and inside yourself. Instead of continuing to say *"When I get to my Weight Goal, I'm going to..."* make a list of what it is you want to do and then really look at why you think you have to wait. I know it's hard for some of us not to worry about things, but it's time to stop worrying about *"how long will this take?"* and *"how will I ever keep it off?"* and *"how will I ever reach my goal?"* All of these statements not only show worry but also show you don't believe you will be able to accomplish them.

Repeat after me,

"I am worth it!"
"I can do this."
"I do deserve this."

Losing weight is a process, and it can be an enjoyable process. Just remember there isn't an on-off switch that we can hit when we get to goal that will make us into a happy person. My view is that the journey is when we should start getting excited and happy.

Happy that we've made the decision to do this for ourselves. Excited that the weight is coming off and maybe one week we tuck in a shirt or we're not out of breath after lugging the groceries in from the car. These are joyful moments, and we need to start getting excited about every single one of them!

And joyful people seem to attract more joy. It's like a magnet.

Password
Protection

For most baby boomers, until recently the word password would bring with it memories of Allen Ludden and the "lightning round." This might explain why so many of us weren't properly prepared as we took those baby steps toward computer use, when first asked to sign on and create a password.

We tried to be savvy enough not to use predictable words, such as our names or our birthdays. And as we timidly explored the Internet highway, different Web sites would invite us to join, requesting a password, often with a different number of letters or a combination of numbers and letters. At the time of selection, these passwords made perfect sense, and we certainly felt we would definitely remember the secret code.

A few were smart enough to maintain a list to refer to when memory failed. For some immature reason, the rest of us relied on our memories, which would continually fail us due to password overload.

Even when we thought we'd gotten the hang of it, there were moments when time was wasted due to our being caught up in the quarterly loop: "Your password will expire in 14 days..." The thought of having to come up with another simple, easy-to-remember code word would sometimes bring with it a rush of panic.

It's as if we started a venture before we learned all of the rules. As we continued exploring, we would sometimes encounter error messages that might bring our progress to a halt. Some of us might have been frustrated by the continual beep signaling wrong entries, so much so that we wanted to take a sledgehammer to said computer.

Once we cooled off, most of us would be wooed back by the vast unexplored capabilities instead of logging off the Internet highway forever.

Obviously with time most of us have overcome our fears. We may not understand how Mapquest knows how to get from our driveway to our cousin's house four states away, but we accept it as we marvel at its brain.

As with most worthwhile accomplishments, getting to this point takes practice, practice, practice. So it's important to swallow the fear and muddle on until our confusion turns into aha's.

If we have other areas of our lives where fear and confusion keep us immobile, it's important to take a moment to analyze what effect this has on our progress in life's journey. Turn to a friend or co-worker who seems to be sailing smoothly along. Ask them their secret. Most times their route isn't so smooth, yet their attitude allows them to deal. Surprisingly, they might be looking at you thinking you have the uncluttered highway. It's as if we have our own Help icon to click on to get support from one another to overcome our current challenges. And yet some of us ignore that aid right within our reach. We either shut down or decide to sink or swim on our own.

A password isn't necessary to open up avenues that will help us. We just have to pass word to a friend or loved one, be it a simple Help that could turn things around. And the great thing is this password doesn't expire.

The Fork in the Road

After years of taking the same roads to and from most destinations, you can pretty much put the car on autopilot and preoccupy your mind with other thoughts—that is, until the highway department decides to throw a wrench into the mix. Recently one of our major thoroughfares, which was torn up and tractor laden for months on end, finally reopened amid cries of joy from commuters far and wide.

As I anticipated no more construction congestion, I naively approached the beautifully paved stretch and expected to move ahead full throttle. My expectations were right on as I zipped by the now-covered "Down to One Lane" signs.

Suddenly confusion replaced my lightheartedness as I became aware of the fact that something was amiss. It only took a few milliseconds to register that my mind map for going from point A to point B had a little detour because now I was going to point C.

The thought of "how did I get here?" was quickly clarified as I noticed several cars behind me slamming on their breaks, trying to get over to another lane. In the grand scheme of making the traffic flow evenly, the fork in the road had been switched: Those who used to take the left fork would now take the right fork and vice versa. I guess I missed the bulletin.

This switch probably made total sense on paper, but had anyone taken into consideration the human element of being attached to habits? Once I was able to turn around, I made the mental note that from here on I would need to be in the left lane at the fork, not the right lane. And being of average intelligence, I thought I would have this snag licked. Out of my sense of neighborly camaraderie, I would mention to anyone I saw, "Did you know they changed the fork on the expressway?" It became the topic at many a get-together in my area, and I felt better as I heard other people had the same experience.

It's been months now since this transition and I need more than both my hands to count how many times I have made the wrong choice. "What's wrong with me?" keeps playing in my brain accompanied by annoyance since the wrong turn brings with it an unnecessary ride over a bridge and a toll on the way back! I have placed two Post-it notes on my steering wheel as a bold reminder: "Left!" for the trip to work and "Right!" for the return.

Habits. Most times we don't even realize we are creatures of them until someone points it out to us. And usually they point out the annoying ones.

However, it's important to recognize we all possess many good habits. Habits get a bad rap since often our good ones become the norm and no one oohs and aahs about them. Those nasty habits that we might want to change are often so embedded that we sometimes feel hopeless and unable to ever switch over to something admirable.

The first step in changing a habit is awareness and then it has to be followed by the desire to change. It's also important to throw in a dash of patience, since most habits die hard.

But just as in the case of my commute, even though I went the wrong way more times than I care to admit, I know I will eventually retrain my brain on what is now acceptable. The same is true of going from a couch potato to an exercise person or from a smoker to a non.

It isn't easy, but it can happen if we make ourselves a priority and believe we can make the changes. Granted there are days I have my doubts, but as long as I concentrate and don't talk to a living soul as I approach the fork, I should eventually make it a new habit that I don't even have to think about.

Which lane are you going to take when the fork splits the road? One might take a little more effort than the other, but the destination might bring you a sense of great achievement.

Don't Settle

During a trip to Italy we were scheduled to spend three days on the Amalfi coast, in the built-into-the-cliffs town of Positano. When we rented a car in Naples, it was suggested we take the longer, more scenic route to our destination. It was a beautiful day, and this sounded like a wonderful idea, so off we went.

For anyone who has never driven in Italy, my recommendation is always have a co-pilot just to read the signs. I was very excited as we reached the signs stating Salerno was around the bend, knowing Positano wasn't far off. We'd read about the cliffs and the curvy roads, so we were ready for them. Since my husband had lived in Italy for two years and was a skilled driver, I knew I was in safe hands.

Obviously we didn't have a clue.

If we had one ninety-degree turn to conquer, we had a hundred. Out of the corner of our eyes, we could catch a glance of a glistening body of water, but neither of us wanted to take our eyes off the road for a fraction of a second.

Maneuvering the curves wasn't the only problem. Try maneuvering a curve with an eighty-passenger bus coming from the other direction as a motorcyclist chatting on a cell phone passes the bus! This wasn't an isolated occurrence. It happened continually along this nightmarish drive.

Neither my husband nor I is a wimp when it comes to tackling the road, but with forty-one kilometers left to our destination I was ready to call a halt to the drive. If I opened my eyes, Amalfi looked okay. We could cancel our reservations in Positano. What was the sense of putting ourselves through this stress when we were supposed to be having a relaxing vacation? Why not cut our losses and settle in here?

Of course for the last ten months I had been visualizing myself sitting on our terrace in Positano, calmly taking in the serenity and beauty. If we stopped now, wouldn't I always wonder if Positano was all that I had dreamed about for so long?

In how many other areas of our lives do we stop our dream journey just short of reaping the rewards of our achievement because the going got tough? We settle, and our settling might not even be such a bad thing, but we'll always wonder if only and what if.

Slowly we made our way, and as Positano came into our sight, we both agreed it had been worth the trip. Many times during our stay there, I found myself smiling as I sat in my chair on our terrace, calmly taking in the serenity and beauty. And to think I almost missed out on this!

Ask yourself, "What am I missing out on?" Then dig in, and go for it! Life is too short to settle.